POLYMER REVIEWS

Editors: H. F. MARK and E. H. IMMERGUT

Additional volumes in preparation

CHEMISTRY AND PHYSICS OF POLYCARBONATES

By HERMANN SCHNELL

Farbenfabriken Bayer A. G., Werk Uerdingen

Krefeld-Uerdingen,

Germany

INTERSCIENCE PUBLISHERS

A DIVISION OF JOHN WILEY & SONS
NEW YORK · LONDON · SYDNEY

Library of Congress Catalog Card Number 64-20086
PRINTED IN THE UNITED STATES OF AMERICA

INTRODUCTION TO THE SERIES

This series was initiated to permit the review of a field of current interest to polymer chemists and physicists *while* the field was still in a state of development. Each author is encouraged to speculate, to present his own opinions and theories, and, in general, to give his work a more "personal flavor" than is customary in the usual reference book or review article. Whenever background material was required to explain a new development in the light of existing and well-known data, the authors have included them, and, as a result, some of the volumes are lengthier than one would expect of a "review."

We hope that the books in this series will generate as much new research as they attempt to review.

H. F. Mark
E. H. Immergut

PREFACE

This book is intended to present with some degree of continuity all the work published through the end of 1962 on the chemistry and physics of polycarbonates. It appeared prudent to undertake this task in the light of the thorough efforts many laboratories have devoted to this family of macromolecular substances in the 10 years since the unique properties of polycarbonates based on 4,4'-dihydroxy-diphenyl methane derivatives were recognized.

The results of these efforts have demonstrated the aromatic polycarbonates to be significantly different in their physical properties, morphology, and crystalline behavior from other thermoplastics. Yet little has been learned regarding the underlying relationships between chemical identity, molecular arrangement, and morphological structure on the one hand and physical properties on the other. To stimulate further work in this area and to present those engaged in it with a reference to the present state of the art are among the more important ambitions of this book.

Although the existing literature has been carefully sifted, it is not reflected in its entirety as one would expect, say, of a literature review. Particularly the sections dealing with processing technology and commercial applications of aromatic polycarbonates were kept brief in view of the extensive coverage these subjects have received elsewhere.

For their valuable suggestions and contributions to the manuscript I am indebted to Dr. L. Bottenbruch, Dr. A. Horbach, Dr. G. Kämpf, Dr. A. Prietzschk, Dr. U. Veiel, and Dr. H. Wunderlich. I also wish to express my sincere appreciation to the staff of Mobay Chemical Company, particularly Mr. Emanuel Wirfel, Mr. P. J. Baker, and Dr. G. F. Baumann, for the competent translation of the text and to the Farbenfabriken Bayer A.G. for their consent to the publication of this book.

Krefeld-Uerdingen, Germany   HERMANN SCHNELL
June 1964

CONTENTS

CONTENTS

I. INTRODUCTION

For the purpose of this book polycarbonates are defined as linear poly-esters of carbonic acid in which the carbonate groups recur in the polymer chain according to the general formula I-1.

(I-1)
$$H\left[-O-R-O-\overset{\overset{\textstyle O}{\|}}{C}-O-R\right]_n-OH$$

Depending on the nature of R, in the above formula the polycarbonates can be subdivided into aliphatic, aliphatic-aromatic, or aromatic poly-carbonates. As indicated by this definition, addition polymers prepared by an ionic or radical polymerization mechanism are not discussed in this book, although they may be derived from monomers containing carbonate groups in addition to reactive carbon-to-carbon double bonds, such as polymers of methyl-vinyl carbonate (1), monomers in which allyl or methallyl alcohol are linked to polyfunctional aliphatic (2), or aromatic (3), hydroxy compounds or hydroxy carbonic acid esters (4), via carbonic acid ester groups.

The data compiled in this book concerning the preparation, physical and chemical properties, fabrication, and applications of polycarbonates are based on the scientific and patent literature through 1962. Unpublished results or private communications are especially noted. Patent applications or patents are listed only under one country, which often is that country in which the application or the patent was first published. The preparations of raw materials or intermediates for polycarbonates are mentioned only for new compounds or if the necessary purity had not previously been obtained. This is especially true for diphenyl carbonate and bisphenol A (4,4'-dihydroxy-diphenyl-2,2-propane).

II. HISTORICAL

The history of polycarbonates is a part of the development of polyesters in general. Polyesters from succinic acid and ethylene glycol were first mentioned in 1863 by Lourenço (5). Vorländer (6) first prepared polyesters from fumaric and maleic acid and ethylene glycol.

Einhorn (7) prepared aromatic polyesters of carbonic acid by reaction of phosgene with resorcinol and hydroquinone in pyridine. Hydroquinone gave an insoluble polymer which melted above 280°C, whereas resorcinol yielded an insoluble polyester which melted with decomposition at 190°C. Bischoff and Hedenstroem (8) obtained the same polyesters by transesterification of hydroquinone or resorcinol with diphenyl carbonate. Aromatic polyesters of carbonic acid were not mentioned again in either the scientific or the patent literature during the next 50 years, probably because of the uninteresting properties of the particular esters investigated originally.

The first attempts to introduce linear polyesters technically were made by Hofmann (9) in 1917. The waxlike polyesters prepared from adipic acid or α-methyladipic acid and ethylene glycol or 1,2-propanediol were intended as substitutes for natural fats and waxes.

In 1929 W. H. Carothers and his co-workers (10) systematically prepared a large number of aliphatic and aromatic-aliphatic polyesters as part of his classical work on polymerization and ring formation. He investigated polyesters of malonic acid, succinic acid, adipic acid, sebacic acid, maleic acid, fumaric acid, and phthalic acid, with ethylene glycol, 1,3-propanediol, 1,6-hexanediol, and 1,10-decanediol as the dihydroxy compounds. Depending upon the particular combination of acid and diol, he obtained low molecular weight polyesters which were viscous liquids or microcrystalline solids with melting points below 100°C.

In 1932 Carothers (11), utilizing a special polycondensation procedure, succeeded in preparing so-called "superpolyesters" which would give films or fibers. These "superpolyesters" could be obtained by esterification of aliphatic dicarboxylic acids with aliphatic dihydroxy compounds or by polycondensation of aliphatic ω-hydroxy carboxylic acids. Carothers also utilized carbonic acid as a bifunctional carboxylic acid. Carothers and van Natta (12) were the first to prepare low melting, low molecular weight microcrystalline polycarbonates by transesterification of aliphatic di-

3

hydroxy compounds with diethyl carbonate or by polymerization of cyclic carbonates of aliphatic dihydroxy compounds. Peterson (13) succeeded in obtaining a low-melting, high molecular weight polycarbonate which would form films or fibers by a rather complicated transesterification of 1,6-hexanediol with dibutyl carbonate. The high molecular weight aliphatic polyesters forming films and fibers did not gain any importance in technology, above all because of their low-melting point.

Linear low molecular weight liquid or low-melting polyesters are utilized as soft resins and as plasticizers, especially for polyvinyl chloride, because of their low volatility, their negligible tendency to migrate to the surface, and their good physiological properties (14). Since 1910 the chemical industry, especially in the United States, England, and Germany, has attempted to develop uses for these easily accessible polyesters. Toward this end, the liquid or low-melting polyesters were converted by crosslinking the linear or branched polyester molecules through primary valence bridges during or after molding to an insoluble and infusible state (15). Thus the so-called glyptal resins which are based on glycerine and phthalic anhydride (16) were developed in the laboratories of General Electric. They are used as adhesives and baking enamels. Another important development in the synthetic coating sector was the introduction by General Electric, and later by the I. G. Farbenindustrie A.G., of low-melting polyesters based on monoglycerides of unsaturated fatty acids, polyfunctional alcohols, and phthalic acid (17). When applied in thin layers at room temperature or slightly elevated temperatures, these polyesters crosslink under the influence of the oxygen in the air to form hard, elastic, water-resistant coatings.

Since 1937 O. Bayer, of Farbenfabriken Bayer A.G., has developed so-called reaction coatings for the paint industry, coating compounds for paper, textiles, leather, and other substrates, adhesives, elastomers of various degrees of hardness and elasticity, and foams—all based on the reaction between low molecular weight linear or branched aliphatic polyesters with terminal hydroxyl groups and polyfunctional isocyanates (18). The so-called diisocyanate "polyaddition reaction" has gained great technical significance and opened new fabrication techniques and application areas for the polyesters involved.

New developments, especially by Pittsburgh Plate Glass and American Cyanamid, opened up the areas of castable and compression moldable polyester resins. For this purpose unsaturated liquid or low-melting polyesters, containing maleic or fumaric acid as unsaturated dicarboxylic acid, are dissolved in monomeric vinyl compounds, especially styrene.

The solutions can be polymerized by radical forming polymerization catalysts at room temperature or slightly elevated temperature with or without applying pressure to obtain colorless, transparent, hard, and elastic articles. Especially useful physical properties are obtained if these crosslinked polymerizates are prepared in the presence of glass fibers. Many attempts were made to utilize carbonic acid as a difunctional carboxylic acid for these low molecular weight liquid or lowmelting polyesters (19), which could be utilized in the subsequent crosslinking reactions. Economic and technical reasons, however, had made it impossible so far to develop a usable carbonic acid polyester of this type.

Thus the scientific world came to the conclusion that polyesters were generally low-melting or liquid compounds which could be used only in conjunction with a subsequent crosslinking reaction, thus giving insoluble and infusible articles.

This conclusion was first disproved in 1941 by Whinfield and Dickson (20), who succeeded in preparing from terephthalic acid and ethylene glycol a high molecular weight, high-melting polyester which is insoluble in most common organic solvents. This polyester has good mechanical and electrical properties and can be formed into films and fibers which can be oriented by stretching. However, the tendency of this polyester to crystallize is so great that unstretched articles become translucent and rather brittle, due to crystallization. Therefore, this polyester cannot be used as a thermoplastic material. The knowledge that high-melting polyesters with good mechanical properties can be prepared inspired a large number of experiments in many laboratories with the goal of producing high-melting thermoplastic polyesters having the characteristics of plastics. The first successful experiments in this direction were made public in 1954 (21). In 1953 H. Schnell and co-workers at the Uerdingen plant of Farbenfabriken Bayer A.G. were the first to prepare high-melting polyesters of carbonic acid with the properties of plastics based on aromatic dihydroxy compounds of the 4,4'-dihydroxy-diphenyl alkane type (22). Farbenfabriken Bayer A.G. applied for a Federal German patent covering the process on October 16, 1953. Patents were granted on this as well as on numerous corresponding foreign applications. In countries granting protection for compositions of matter, such as in the United States of America, the patents also cover the polycarbonates as such.

The General Electric Company also conducted research in the area of aromatic polyesters of carbonic acid (23) and noticed the favorable properties of polycarbonates based on 4,4'-dihydroxy-diphenyl alkanes.

The outstanding properties of these polycarbonates and the easy accessibility of the intermediates led to a rapid development of technical procedures to produce intermediates of the required purity and the final polymers.

In the latter part of 1958 Farbenfabriken Bayer A.G. began commercial production of polycarbonates in their plant in Uerdingen, using preparative methods developed in the laboratories. The production of polycarbonate based on 4,4'-dihydroxy-diphenyl-2,2-propane was also started early in 1960 by the Mobay Chemical Company, New Martinsville, West Virginia (24). Using their own process, the General Electric Company began production of the same polyester in late 1960 in a plant in Mount Vernon, Indiana (25). Industrial units are being planned or constructed in Japan at the present time.

In recent years Eastman Kodak Company (26) described linear, thermoplastic, aromatic-aliphatic polycarbonates which were based on oxyalkylated aromatic dihydroxy compounds. These high-melting polycarbonates show a great tendency to crystallize, so that their application so far is probably limited to highly stretched films or fibers.

References

1. F. E. Künig, (to Pittsburgh Plate Glass Co.), U. S. Pat. 2,370,549 (1945).
2. I. E. Muskat et al. (to Pittsburgh Plate Glass Co.), U. S. Pats. 2,370,567, 2,370,571, 2,370,574, 2,379,250, 2,384,115, 2,384,123, 2,385,930, 2,385,932, 2,387,933 (1945).
3. I. E. Muskat et al. (to Pittsburgh Plate Glass Co.), U. S. Pats. 2,370,566, 2,370,573, 2,379,251, 2,384,116–118, 2,384,126, 2,385,931, 2,385,934, 2,387,931 (1945), 2,401,581 (1946).
4. J. A. Brally and F. B. Pope (to B. F. Goodrich Co.), U. S. Pats. 2,455,652–653 (1948), 2,587,437 (1952); F. J. Held and R. P. Blaine (to B. F. Goodrich Co.), U. S. Pat. 2,468,975 (1949); E. J. Carlson (to B. F. Goodrich Co.), U. S. Pats. 2,529,867 (1950), 2,587,442 (1952); F. B. Pope (to B. F. Goodrich Co.), U. S. Pat. 2,568,658 (1951).
5. M. A.-V. Lourenço, *Ann. chim. phys.* **67**, 257 (1863).
6. D. Vorländer, *Ann.* **280**, 167 (1894).
7. A. Einhorn, *Ann.* **300**, 135 (1898).
8. C. A. Bischoff and A. v. Hedenstroem, *Ber.* **35**, 3431 (1902).
9. F. Hofmann (to I. G. Farbenindustrie A.G.), Ger. Pat. 318,222 (1917); *Friedl.* **13**, 184 (1923).
10. W. H. Carothers and J. A. Arvin, *J. Am. Chem. Soc.* **51**, 3560 (1929). *Collected Papers of W. H. Carothers on Polymerization,* H. Mark and G. Stafford Whitby, eds., Interscience Publishers, New York, 1940.
11. W. H. Carothers and J. W. Hill, *J. Am. Chem. Soc.* **54**, 1559, 1566, 1579 (1932).
12. W. H. Carothers and F. J. van Natta, *J. Am. Chem. Soc.* **52**, 314 (1930).
13. W. R. Peterson (to E. I. du Pont de Nemours & Co.), U.S. Pat. 2,210,817 (1940).

14. W. M. Lanham (to Carbide and Carbon Corp.), U. S. Pats. 2,512,722–723 (1950).
15. H. Schnell, *Kunststoffe—Plastics* **7**, 305 (1960).
16. M. Callahan (to General Electric Co.), U. S. Pat. 1,091,732 (1914); M. J. Callahan (to General Electric Co.), U.S. Pats. 1,108,329–331 (1914).
17. W. C. Arsem (to General Electric Co.), U. S. Pat. 1,098,777 (1914); K. B. Howell (to General Electric Co.), U. S. Pat. 1,098,728 (1914); R. H. Kienle (to General Electric Co.), U. S. Pat. 1,893,873 (1927); K. Ott, F. Frick, and H. Bernard (to I. G. Farbenindustrie A.G.), Ger. Pat. 547,517 (1932).
18. O. Bayer et al., *Ann.* **549**, 286 (1941); *Angew. Chem.* **A 59**, 257 (1947); *Angew. Chem.* **62**, 57 (1950) and **64**, 523 (1952); R. Hebermehl, *Farben, Lacke, Anstrichstoffe* **2**, 123 (1948); A. Hoechtlen, *Kunststoffe* **40**, 221 (1950) and **42**, 303 (1952); E. Müller, *Kunststoffe* **41**, 13 (1951).
19. H. Krzikalla (to Badische Anilin-und Sodafabrik A.G.), Ger. Pat. 887,119 (1953); Ch. L. Wilson and C. J. Benning (to Hudson Foam Plastics Corp.), Ger. Pat. Appl. 1,022,790 (1958); Brit. Pat. 837,895 (1960); S. F. Marrian (to Imperial Chemical Industries Ltd.), Brit. Pat. 650,002 (1951).
20. J. R. Whinfield and J. T. Dickson, Brit. Pat. 578,079 (1946); J. R. Whinfield, *Nature* **158**, 930 (1946); *Endeavour* **11**, 29 (1952).
21. Belg. Pat. 532,543 to Farbenfabriken Bayer A.G. (1954).
22. H. Schnell, *Angew. Chem.* **68**, 633 (1956); H. Schnell, L. Bottenbruch, and H. Krimm (to Farbenfabriken Bayer A.G.), U. S. Pat. 3,028,365 (1962).
23. D. W. Fox (to General Electric Co.), Australian Pat. 221,192 (1959).
24. Anon., *Mod. Plastics* **36**, 43 (September 1958).
25. Anon., *Chem. Eng.* **14**, 174 (1960).
26. D. D. Reynolds et al. (to Eastman Kodak Co.), U. S. Pats. 2,789,964–967, 2,789,969–972 (1957).

III. CHEMISTRY OF POLYCARBONATES

1. ALIPHATIC POLYCARBONATES

A. Preparation of Aliphatic Polycarbonates

Among others, the following methods have been used to prepare aliphatic polycarbonates: reaction of aliphatic dihydroxy compounds with phosgene or with bis-chlorocarbonic acid esters of aliphatic dihydroxy compounds in organic solvents in the absence or presence of acid binding materials; transesterification of aliphatic dihydroxy compounds with dialkyl- or diaryl-carbonates; polymerization of cyclic carbonates of aliphatic dihydroxy compounds.

1. Preparation of Aliphatic Polycarbonates by Phosgenation

The following reactions may occur if aliphatic dihydroxy compounds are reacted with phosgene as such or dissolved in inert solvents:

(III-1) $HO-(CH_2)_n-OH + COCl_2 \rightarrow HO-(CH_2)_n-O-\overset{\overset{\textstyle O}{\|}}{C}-Cl + HCl$

(III-2) $HO-(CH_2)_n-O-\overset{\overset{\textstyle O}{\|}}{C}-Cl + COCl_2 \rightarrow$

$$Cl-\overset{\overset{\textstyle O}{\|}}{C}-O-(CH_2)_n-O-\overset{\overset{\textstyle O}{\|}}{C}-Cl + HCl$$

(III-3) $xHO-(CH_2)_n-O-\overset{\overset{\textstyle O}{\|}}{C}-Cl \rightarrow$

$$H-\left[O-(CH_2)_n-O-\overset{\overset{\textstyle O}{\|}}{C}-\right]_x Cl + (x-1)HCl$$

(III-4) $xCl-\overset{\overset{\textstyle O}{\|}}{C}-O-(CH_2)_n-O-\overset{\overset{\textstyle O}{\|}}{C}-Cl + xHO-(CH_2)_n-OH \rightarrow$

$$H-\left[O-(CH_2)_n-O-\overset{\overset{\textstyle O}{\|}}{C}-O-(CH_2)_n-O-\overset{\overset{\textstyle O}{\|}}{C}-\right]Cl + (2x-1)HCl$$

(III-5) $HO-(CH_2)_n-O-\overset{\overset{\textstyle O}{\|}}{C}-Cl \rightarrow (CH_2)_n \begin{matrix} O \\ \diagup \quad \diagdown \\ \diagdown \quad \diagup \\ O \end{matrix} C=O + HCl$

9

(III-6) $HO—(CH_2)_n—OH + HCl \rightarrow HO—(CH_2)_n—Cl + H_2O$

(III-7) $HO—(CH_2)_n—O—\overset{\overset{\displaystyle O}{\|}}{C}—Cl \rightarrow HO—(CH_2)_n—Cl + CO_2$

The particular aliphatic dihydroxy compound used, as well as the reaction conditions, will determine which end-products are formed. The aliphatic hydroxyl group usually reacts fast enough with phosgene below 50°C to form chlorocarbonic acid esters and HCl. In many cases the reaction is so fast that it can be carried out at temperatures below 0°C. The bis-chlorocarbonic acid esters can be obtained in good yields by the reactions III-1 and III-2 if aliphatic hydroxy compounds are added to liquid phosgene or solutions of phosgene in inert solvents (1). Ethylene glycol and other aliphatic 1,2-dihydroxy compounds, however, have a great tendency to form a 5-membered ring according to III-5, so that even under these conditions cyclic carbonates (dioxolones) are formed besides the bis-chlorocarbonic acid esters (2). If phosgene is added to aliphatic dihydroxy compounds, which may be dissolved in inert solvents, at low temperatures the 5- or 6-membered cyclic carbonates are obtained from the 1,2- and 1,3-dihydroxy compounds in good yields. However, dihydroxy compounds with OH-groups separated by more than 4 carbon atoms result in mixtures of bis-chlorocarbonic acid esters with chlorine-containing, higher boiling by-products. High molecular weight chlorine-free polycarbonates are not accessible by this route. The reason for this is that the phosgene and the aliphatic chlorocarbonic acid esters have different reactivity toward hydroxyl groups.

As mentioned above, phosgene reacts rapidly at low temperatures with aliphatic hydroxyl groups to form chlorocarbonic esters. Aliphatic chlorocarbonic esters react considerably slower with aliphatic hydroxy compounds, to form carbonic acid esters, so that this latter reaction has to be carried out at elevated temperatures to speed it up. However, at temperatures above 50°C the hydroxyl groups can be substituted by chlorine, as shown in formulas III-6 and III-7. This leads to the formation of chlorine-containing monofunctional hydroxy compounds, which can act as chain terminators, so that the polycondensation reaction, as shown in formulas III-3 and III-4, will be stopped at relatively low degrees of polymerization. Furthermore, the water formed according to formula III-6 will tend to hydrolyze phosgene and chlorocarbonic esters.

(III-8) $COCl_2 + H_2O \rightarrow CO_2 + 2HCl$

(III-9) $RO\overset{\overset{\displaystyle O}{\|}}{C}—Cl + H_2O \rightarrow R—OH + CO_2 + HCl$

The reaction of phosgene or chlorocarbonic esters with water is faster than with aliphatic hydroxy compounds if carried out under the same conditions. It is therefore impossible to produce chlorocarbonic acid esters, cyclic carbonates, or polycarbonates by phosgenation of aliphatic dihydroxy compounds in the presence of water or aqueous alkali. This is true even when the reaction is carried out in a two-phase mixture in the presence of an inert, water-immiscible solvent. The desired reaction products are not obtained at all or only in poor yields.

The reaction of aliphatic dihydroxy compounds in inert solvents, such as toluene or xylene, with phosgene at high temperatures in the presence of finely distributed carbonates, bicarbonates, or hydroxides of alkali or alkaline-earth metals yields low molecular weight by polycarbonates with terminal hydroxyl groups, provided the water formed during neutralization is quickly removed from the reaction mixture (3).

In order to obtain aliphatic polycarbonates by phosgenating aliphatic dihydroxy compounds at low temperature, it is necessary to accelerate the reaction. It is well known that pyridine and other tertiary amines, such as dimethylaniline, form ionic adducts with phosgene and chlorocarbonic acid esters, which are more reactive toward aliphatic hydroxy compounds than the carbonic acid derivatives themselves (4).

The ionic adducts formed by reaction of pyridine with phosgene or chlorocarbonic acid esters (5) are especially suited to the preparation of neutral carbonic acid esters and polycarbonates.

(III-10)

(III-11)

The adducts formed according to formula III-11 are considerably more reactive than the corresponding chlorocarbonic acid esters. The reaction of these adducts with hydroxy compounds yields carbonic acid esters and pyridine hydrochloride (see formula III-12).

It is not necessary to produce adducts as such or in solution and then to react them with hydroxy compounds. It is necessary only to introduce phosgene or chlorocarbonic acid esters into a solution of the hydroxy compound in pyridine or into a mixture of pyridine with an inert solvent.

(III-12)
$$\left[R-O-\overset{\overset{\textstyle O}{\|}}{C}-N\overset{(+)}{\diagup}\bigcirc \right] Cl^{(-)} \;+\; R'OH$$

$$\longrightarrow \; R-O-\overset{\overset{\textstyle O}{\|}}{C}-O-R' \;+\; \left[\bigcirc \overset{(+)}{N}-H \right] Cl^{(-)}$$

Pyridine hydrochloride will not react with phosgene or chlorocarbonic acid ester to form the reactive adducts. It is therefore necessary to use at least one mole of pyridine, based on the amount of chlorocarbonic acid ester, or two moles of pyridine, based on the amount of phosgene. These reactions have to be carried out in the absence of water because the adducts react rapidly with water decomposing to CO_2 and pyridine hydrochloride. Side reactions were observed, especially at elevated temperatures, when tertiary amines were used as acid binding materials in the phosgenation and when these amines contained one or several alkyl groups with a small number of carbon atoms. These side reactions were due to the formation of alkyl chlorides and carbamic acid esters by a reaction of the chlorocarbonic acid esters with these amines (6):

(III-13)
$$\underset{H_3C}{\overset{R}{\diagdown}}N + R'-O-\overset{\overset{\textstyle O}{\|}}{C}-Cl \; \longrightarrow \; \underset{R}{\overset{R}{\diagdown}}N-\overset{\overset{\textstyle O}{\|}}{C}-O-R' + CH_3Cl$$

For the preparation of aliphatic polycarbonates the aliphatic dihydroxy compound is dissolved in a mixture of an inert solvent, such as chloroform, and 2 moles of pyridine per mole of dihydroxy compound. One mole of phosgene is added at or below room temperature. The viscous solution is washed with dilute HCl and then with water and finally dried. The polycarbonate can be isolated by evaporation of the solvent.

Cyclic carbonates are obtained in good yields by phosgenation in the presence of tertiary amines of those aliphatic dihydroxy compounds, which are capable of forming 5- or 6-membered cyclic carbonates. Aliphatic 1,4-dihydroxy compounds can also form cyclic carbonates when the Ruggli-Ziegler dilution principle is used.

Sarel, Pohoryles, and Ben-Shoshan (7) obtained the 7- and 14-membered cyclic carbonates, besides low molecular weight polycarbonate, when they added a solution of phosgene in toluene to a dilute solution of 1,4-butanediol and antipyrine in chloroform at 40–50°C.

2. Preparation of Aliphatic Polycarbonates by Reaction of Bis-Chlorocarbonic Acid Esters of Aliphatic Dihydroxy Compounds with Aliphatic Dihydroxy Compounds

During the reaction of bis-chlorocarbonic acid esters of aliphatic di-hydroxy compounds with aliphatic dihydroxy compounds at elevated temperatures the substitution reaction III-6, in which hydroxyl groups are exchanged by chlorine, can be partially eliminated by carrying out the reaction *in vacuo,* so that the HCl formed is immediately taken out of the reaction mixture. In this manner Krzikalla and Merkel (8) ob-tained low molecular weight aliphatic polycarbonates, as indicated by the following procedure:

> 990 parts by weight of 1,4-butanediol are added over a 5-hour period to 2365 parts by weight of bis-chlorocarbonic acid ester of 1,4-butane-diol with constant stirring at 75°C and 35 mm Hg. The whole reaction mixture is then slowly heated to 220°C so that the pressure remains approximately constant. After the HCl formation has stopped the mixture is cooled. A waxlike polyester with a melting point of 62–65°C and a molecular weight of more than 2000 is obtained.

The reaction of aliphatic dihydroxy compounds with bis-chlorocar-bonic acid esters of aliphatic dihydroxy compounds in inert solvents, such as toluene or xylene, at elevated temperature in the presence of finely distributed carbonates, bicarbonates, or hydroxides of alkali or alkaline-earth metals also yields low molecular weight polycarbonates with terminal OH-groups, provided the water formed during neutralization is quickly removed from the reaction mixture (3).

The reaction of bis-chlorocarbonic acid esters of aliphatic dihydroxy compounds with aliphatic dihydroxy compounds in the presence of tertiary amines as it has been described in the preceding paragraph is better suited for the preparation of high molecular weight aliphatic polycarbonates. Because of their thermal instability it is difficult to pre-pare bis-chlorocarbonic acid esters of aliphatic dihydroxy compounds in a sufficiently high purity for the preparation of high molecular weight polycarbonates. Therefore the preparation of aliphatic polycarbonates by this route is of interest only when different dihydroxy compounds are to be used to form a regular copolymer with alternating monomer units.

$$\text{(III-14)} \quad x\text{Cl}-\overset{\overset{\text{O}}{\|}}{\text{C}}-\text{O}-\text{R}-\text{O}-\overset{\overset{\text{O}}{\|}}{\text{C}}-\text{Cl} + x\text{HO}-\text{R}'-\text{OH} \xrightarrow{\text{Pyridine}}$$

$$\text{H}-\left[\text{O}-\text{R}'-\text{O}-\overset{\overset{\text{O}}{\|}}{\text{C}}-\text{O}-\text{R}-\text{O}-\overset{\overset{\text{O}}{\|}}{\text{C}}-\right]_x\text{Cl} + (2x-1)\text{ Pyridine HC}$$

For the preparation of aliphatic polycarbonates the phosgene or bis-chlorocarbonic acid esters of aliphatic dihydroxy compounds can be substituted by compounds which may react in the same way, such as chloroformic acid-trichloromethylester (diphosgene), bis-trichloromethyl carbonate, or bis-trichloromethyl carbonates of aliphatic dihydroxy compounds (9).

(III-15)

$$O=C\begin{matrix} O-CCl_3 \\ \\ Cl \end{matrix} \qquad O=C\begin{matrix} O-CCl_3 \\ \\ O-CCl_3 \end{matrix}$$

$$Cl_3C-O-\overset{\overset{\displaystyle O}{\|}}{C}-O-R-O-\overset{\overset{\displaystyle O}{\|}}{C}-O-CCl_3$$

3. Preparation of Aliphatic Polycarbonates by Transesterification of Aliphatic Dihydroxy Compounds with Carbonic Acid Diesters

The most important method of preparation of aliphatic polycarbonates is the transesterification of aliphatic dihydroxy compounds with equimolar amounts of carbonic acid diesters:

(III-16)

$$x HO-(CH_2)_n-OH + xR-O-\overset{\overset{\displaystyle O}{\|}}{C}-O-R$$

$$\nearrow \quad x(CH_2)_n\begin{matrix} O \\ \diagup \quad \diagdown \\ \quad C=O \\ \diagdown \quad \diagup \\ O \end{matrix} + 2xROH$$

$$\searrow \quad H\left[-O-(CH_2)_n-O-\overset{\overset{\displaystyle O}{\|}}{C}-\right]_x OR +$$
$$(2x-1)\ ROH$$

Depending on the particular aliphatic dihydroxy compounds used in this reaction and the conditions, cyclic carbonates, cyclic carbonates and polycarbonates, or only polycarbonates are obtained. Carothers, van Natta, and Hill (10) transesterified aliphatic dihydroxy compounds of the general formula $HO-(CH_2)_n-OH$, where $n = 2, 3, 4, 5, 6, 7, 8, 9, 11, 12, 13, 14,$ and 18, diethylene glycol, triethylene glycol, and p-xylylene glycol with diethyl carbonate or dibutyl carbonate at temperatures between 120 and 160°C, utilizing the catalytic action of sodium alcoholates, produced in the reaction mixture from the dihydroxy compounds used. Vacuum was used in many cases during the latter part of the transesterification to remove completely the alcohols split off. In this manner they obtained the cyclic glycolcarbonate from ethylene glycol; from 1,3-trimethylene glycol they obtained the cyclic trimethylene glycolcarbonate. However, the aliphatic dihydroxy compounds in which the OH-groups were separated by more than three CH_2-groups resulted in poly-carbonates with molecular weights below 3000. Sarel and co-workers (7) investigated the influence of reaction conditions and structure of the aliphatic dihydroxy compounds on the formation of cyclic carbonates or polycarbonates during the transesterification with dialkyl carbonates; 2,2-dimethyl-, 2-methyl-2-n-propyl-, and 2-methyl-2-isoamyl-1,3-pro-panediol with diethyl carbonate in the presence of small amounts of alka-line catalysts form only polycarbonates. If large amounts of catalysts are used, the corresponding 6-membered cyclic carbonates are also obtained; 2,3-diethyl-, 2-ethyl-2-phenyl-1,3-propanediol, 2,4-pentane-diol, and 1,3-butanediol yield only 6-membered cyclic carbonates, inde-pendent of the reaction conditions; 1,4-butanediol forms the 7-membered cyclic carbonate as well as 1,4-bis-ethoxycarbonyloxy-butane if it is transesterified with diethyl carbonate in toluene. The monoesters are formed first in the reaction of aliphatic dihydroxy compounds with dialkyl carbonates. The reaction conditions and the structure of the dihydroxy compounds determine whether the monoesters form cyclic carbonates or polycarbonates. Increase of the rate of reaction and use of the dilution principle favor the formation of cyclic compounds. The formation of cyclic polycarbonates from 1,3-propanediol derivates can be favored by bulky substituents on C_2 or substituents on C_1 and C_3.

Dialkyl carbonates will not transesterify with aliphatic dihydroxy compounds in the absence of catalysts even at elevated temperatures. The reaction is feasible only in the presence of strong basic catalysts, such as sodium methylate, and at temperatures between 120 and 220°C. At these temperatures, however, the carbonic acid esters of low alcohols, such as diethyl or dibutyl carbonate, are volatile, so that a part of the carbonic acid esters are taken out of the reaction mixture together with the alcohol split off. This causes the excess of dihydroxy compound to react as a chain terminator and prevents the formation of high molecular weight polycarbonates. Even if this were prevented by special precautions (11) high molecular weight polycarbonates are not obtained in this way because the highly alkaline catalysts, used during the transesterification of the dialkyl carbonate, tend to degrade and decompose the aliphatic carbonate at the necessary transesterification temperatures. The reactions involved as well as the decomposition products obtained are discussed in more detail in the following paragraph.

Peterson (12) modified the transesterification procedure used by Carothers to eliminate the influence of the alkaline transesterification catalyst in the last stages of the transesterification at high temperatures.

He used sodium alcoholates and a nonvolatile, water-insoluble carboxylic acid or a carboxylic acid ester in an amount not equivalent to the alcoholates used as transesterification catalysts. He dissolved the low molecular weight polycarbonate in an inert solvent after the larger portion of the alcohol had been split off during the transesterification with diethyl carbonate and removed all alkali by washing with dilute HCl and water. Then he finished the transesterification, after distilling off the solvent, at temperatures up to 200°C under reduced pressure and the catalytic action of the carboxylic acid. He was able to produce film- and fiber-forming polycarbonates from aliphatic dihydroxy compounds in which the OH-groups were separated by more than three CH_2-groups.

The method for producing high molecular weight aliphatic polycarbonates is greatly simplified by using diaryl carbonates for the transesterification with aliphatic dihydroxy compounds. Piepenbrink (13) found that aliphatic dihydroxy compounds can be transesterified with diphenyl carbonate without catalysts and at relatively low temperatures. High molecular weight film- or fiber-forming aliphatic polycarbonates can be produced if pure raw materials are used. Thus a colorless melt, which solidifies to an opaque, horny mass, can be obtained, if 18.3 parts by weight of 1,6-hexanediol are transesterified with 32.1 parts by weight of diphenyl carbonate, with stirring and in the absence of oxygen, at 180–200°C and a pressure of 100–0.4 mm Hg, within 4 hours. Phenol is eliminated as a by-product. The polycarbonate obtained has a relative viscosity of 1.414, as measured in methylene chloride at 25°C in a 0.5% solution. The polycarbonate melts at 55–60°C and shows a second-order transition temperature of −5°C. It is also possible to produce aliphatic polycarbonates or polycarbonate copolymers by transesterification of dihydroxy compounds with bisalkyl or bisaryl carbonates of the same or other dihydroxy compounds.

$$(\text{III-17}) \quad x\text{HO—R—OH} + x\text{R}'\text{—O—}\overset{\overset{\text{O}}{\|}}{\text{C}}\text{—O—R}''\text{—O—}\overset{\overset{\text{O}}{\|}}{\text{C}}\text{—O—R}' \rightarrow$$

$$x\text{H}\left[\text{—O—R—O—}\overset{\overset{\text{O}}{\|}}{\text{C}}\text{—O—R}''\text{—O—}\overset{\overset{\text{O}}{\|}}{\text{C}}\right]_x\text{—O—R}' + (2x - 1)\text{R}'\text{—OH}$$

M. Gawlak et al. (14) transesterified the *cis*- and *trans*-isomers of 2,2,4,4-tetramethyl cyclobutane-1,3-diol as well as mixtures of the two isomers with the bisethyl carbonates of the same dihydroxy compounds under the influence of alkaline catalysts and obtained high molecular weight polycarbonates, while ethyl alcohol, CO_2, and 2,2,4-trimethyl-3-pentenal were split off.

(III-18) xHO—CH   HC—OH +

(with the diamond-structure groups having CH_3, CH_3 on top carbon C and CH_3, CH_3 on bottom carbon C)

$$+ xCH_3—CH_2—O—\overset{O}{\underset{\|}{C}}—O—CH \quad HC—O—\overset{O}{\underset{\|}{C}}—O—CH_2—CH_3$$

$$\longrightarrow \quad H\left[—O—CH \quad HC—O—\overset{O}{\underset{\|}{C}}—O—CH \quad HC—O—\overset{O}{\underset{\|}{C}}—\right]_x O—CH_2—CH_3 + (2x-1)CH_3—CH_2—OH$$

The formation of 2,2,4-trimethyl-3-pentenal and CO_2 as by-products, which reduce the polymer yield, is due to the side reaction shown in Formula III-19.

$$(III-19) \quad \ldots O—\overset{O}{\underset{\|}{C}}—O—CH \quad HC—O—\overset{O}{\underset{\|}{C}}—O—CH \quad HC—OH$$

$$\rightarrow \quad \ldots O—\overset{O}{\underset{\|}{C}}—O—CH \quad HC—OH + CO_2 + HC \quad C$$

As in this reaction, which probably takes place on the basis of an ionic mechanism, a new hydroxyl group is formed at the end of the chain. It does not prevent the formation of high molecular weight polycarbonates but reduces their yield. The properties of the polymer are described in section III, 1, B.

4. Preparation of Aliphatic Polycarbonates by Polycondensation of Bisalkyl or Bisaryl Carbonates of Aliphatic Dihydroxy Compounds

The presence of aliphatic dihydroxy compounds in the reaction mixture during the polycondensation at elevated temperatures can be avoided if the polycondensation is carried out with bisalkyl or bisaryl carbonates of aliphatic dihydroxy compounds which form polycarbonates by splitting off dialkyl or diaryl carbonates.

$$(\text{III-20}) \quad x\text{R—O—}\overset{\overset{\text{O}}{\|}}{\text{C}}\text{—O—(CH}_2)_n\text{—O—}\overset{\overset{\text{O}}{\|}}{\text{C}}\text{—O—R}$$

$$\rightarrow \quad \text{R—O—}\overset{\overset{\text{O}}{\|}}{\text{C}}\Big[\text{O—(CH}_2)_n\text{—O—}\overset{\overset{\text{O}}{\|}}{\text{C}}\text{—}\Big]_x\text{O—R} + (x-1)\text{R—O—}\overset{\overset{\text{O}}{\|}}{\text{C}}\text{—O—R}$$

R = alkyl or aryl

This procedure has the advantage that the reaction is carried out under exactly stoichiometric conditions during the entire polycondensation and that the decomposition of aliphatic dihydroxy compounds during the polycondensation at elevated temperatures is avoided. By this method Reynolds and Van Den Berghe (15) were able to produce film- and fiber-forming polycarbonates of penta-, hexa-, and decamethylene glycol, even when highly alkaline transesterification catalysts, such as sodium methylate or lithium methylate, were used at temperatures up to 240°C under reduced pressure.

The bisalkyl or bisaryl carbonates of the aliphatic dihydroxy compounds used as raw materials in this reaction are obtained by transesterification of aliphatic dihydroxy compounds with an excess of diaryl or dialkyl carbonate or by reaction of alkyl or aryl chlorocarbonic acid esters with aliphatic dihydroxy compounds in pyridine.

5. Preparation of Aliphatic Polycarbonates by Polymerization of Cyclic Carbonates

Cyclic carbonates of aliphatic dihydroxy compounds with larger than 5-membered rings can be polymerized. These carbonates can be obtained by phosgenation of aliphatic dihydroxy compounds (section III, 1, A, 1), by tranesterification of aliphatic dihydroxy compounds with carbonic acid diesters (section III, 1, A, *3*), or by depolymerization of aliphatic polycarbonate (section III, 1, B). Carothers and van Natta (10) obtained a polytrimethyleneglycolcarbonate by heating cyclic 1,3-trimethylene-glycolcarbonate in the presence of alkaline catalysts, such as potassium carbonate. Hill and Carothers (10) prepared the corresponding poly-carbonates from the cyclic carbonates of deca-, dodeca-, trideca-, and tetradecamethyleneglycols and from the dimeric cyclic carbonates of hexa- and decamethyleneglycol.

(III-21)

$$R\!-\!\left[O\!-\!(CH_2)_n\!-\!O\!-\!\overset{\overset{\displaystyle O}{\|}}{C}\!-\right]_x\!O\!-\!R$$

n = at least 3, R = H or alkyl

Water or aliphatic hydroxy compounds are necessary for chain ter-mination. They can be present in the monomer or formed during heating, or they have to be added.

The polymerization of cyclic carbonates can be greatly hindered by certain substituents on the ring carbon atoms, as has also been shown for other cyclic monomers which can polymerize by ring opening. Thus cyclic carbonates of 2,2-disubstituted 1,3-propanediols show only a negligible tendency to polymerize (7).

Five-membered cyclic carbonates can also form aliphatic polycarbon-ates under special conditions (16). Thus relatively low molecular weight polycarbonates of the general nature of formula III-22 with hydroxyl end groups can be obtained from cyclic ethylene glycol carbonate when heated under pressure to approximately 250°C in the presence of 0.01–0.2 mole (based on glycol carbonate) of a compound with at least two active hydrogen atoms, such as ethylene glycol, and an alkaline catalyst.

(III-22)

$$HO\!-\!(CH_2\!-\!CH_2\!-\!O\!-\!)_x\overset{\overset{\displaystyle O}{\|}}{C}\!-\!O\!-\!(CH_2\!-\!CH_2\!-\!O\!-\!)_y\overset{\overset{\displaystyle O}{\|}}{C}\!-\!O\!-\!(CH_2\!-\!CH_2\!-\!O\!-\!)_z\ldots OH$$

The pressure increases during the reaction due to the splitting off of carbon dioxide. Apparently this reaction is not a polymerization of the

5-membered cyclic carbonate, but the ring first splits off carbon dioxide to form polyglycol ethers.

$$\text{(III-23)} \quad HO\text{---}CH_2\text{---}CH_2\text{---}OH + \begin{array}{c} CH_2\text{---}O \\ \\ CH_2\text{---}O \end{array}\!\!\!\!\!\!\!\!\!\!\!\!\Big\rangle C{=}O$$

$$\xrightarrow[OH^-]{} \quad HO[\text{---}CH_2\text{---}CH_2\text{---}O]_{x+1}\text{---}H + xCO_2$$

These polyglycol ethers can transesterify with additional cyclic carbonate to form alkylene glycol and carbonic acid esters.

$$\text{(III-24)} \quad 2HO(\text{---}CH_2\text{---}CH_2\text{---}O)_x\text{---}H + \begin{array}{c} CH_2\text{---}O \\ \\ CH_2\text{---}O \end{array}\!\!\!\!\!\!\!\!\!\!\!\!\Big\rangle C{=}O \quad \rightarrow$$

$$HO(\text{---}CH_2\text{---}CH_2\text{---}O)_x\overset{\overset{\displaystyle O}{\|}}{\text{---}C}\text{---}O(\text{---}CH_2\text{---}CH_2\text{---}O)_x\text{---}H + HO\text{---}CH_2\text{---}CH_2\text{---}OH$$

Thus rather low molecular weight polycarbonates with hydroxyl end groups are formed in a number of reaction steps which are not well understood. The polycarbonates contain polyglycol ether segments.

B. Properties of Aliphatic Polycarbonates

Because of the low polarity of the carbonic acid ester group, aliphatic polycarbonates are, at room temperature, generally viscous liquids or microcrystalline, low-melting masses with a relatively narrow melting range. The polycarbonates from the isomeric 2,2,4,4-tetramethyl cyclo-butane-1,3-diols are an exception. The polycarbonate from the *trans*-isomer is a highly crystalline powder (about 90% crystallinity) with a crystalline melting point of more than 360°C, and the polycarbonate from the *cis*-isomer is a crystalline powder (about 50% crystallinity) with a crystalline melting point of 253°C (14). (See Table III-1.)

The melting ranges reported above are general guides only. Almost all the polycarbonates investigated were of low molecular weight. At low-molecular weights the melting point of macromolecular compounds quite often increases with increasing molecular weight and becomes independent of the molecular weight only above a characteristic value of the molecular weight. Most aliphatic polycarbonates melt below 120°C. The second-order transition temperature of most aliphatic polycarbonates is low. The second-order transition temperature for a high molecular weight polycarbonate from 1,6-hexanedoil (section III, 1, A, *3*) was —9°C, as

TABLE III-1
Melting Range of Aliphatic Polycarbonates

Polycarbonate made from	Low molecular weight	Film or fiber forming	Melting range [°C]	References
$HO(-CH_2)_3-OH$	+		38–45	(10)
$HO(-CH_2)_4-OH$	+		59	(10)
$HO(-CH_2)_4-OH$		+	60	(15)
$HO(-CH_2)_5-OH$	+		44–46	(10)
$HO(-CH_2)_6-OH$		+	55–60	(10)
$HO(-CH_2)_{16}-OH$	+		55	(10)
$HO-CH_2-CH_2-O-CH_2-CH_2-OH$	+		Liquid	(10,12)
$HO-CH_2-\overset{\displaystyle CH_3}{\underset{\displaystyle CH_3}{C}}-CH_2-OH$		+	107–119	(7)
$HO-CH_2-\overset{\displaystyle CH_3}{\underset{\displaystyle (CH_2)_2}{\underset{\displaystyle CH_3}{C}}}-CH_2-OH$	+		Liquid	(7)
cis		+	253 (crystalline m.p.)	(14)
trans		+	>360 (crystalline m.p.)	(14)

measured by the dilatometric method in silicone oil. Most of the aliphatic polycarbonates, which are solids at room temperature, can be crystallized. If cooled from a melt, they form opaque solids. The melting points of partially crystallized high molecular weight compounds are, *inter alia*, dependent on the degree of crystallinity and therefore on their thermal history. Thus polycarbonate made from 2,2-dimethyl-1,3-propanediol will melt at 107 to 109°C, if quickly cooled from its melt. If the same polymer is conditioned for one week at 100°C, the melting range increases to 117–119°C (7). Aliphatic polycarbonates from ether diols, such as diethylene glycol or triethylene glycol, are liquid. Unsymmetrically branched dihydroxy compounds, such as 2-methyl-2-n-propyl-1,3-propanediol, also form liquid polycarbonates. The melting ranges of the polycarbonates made from symmetrically branched 2,2-dimethyl-1,3-propanediol and from cis- and trans-2,2,4,4-tetramethyl cyclobutane-1,3-diol are surprisingly high. Apparently, in these polycarbonates the melting ranges are increased because of a stiffer polymer back-bone as well as a lowered flexibility due to the pendant methyl groups. (We will see a similar phenomenon with aromatic polycarbonates.) The behavior of the polycarbonate from 2,2-dimethyl-1,3-propanediol during crystallization is also different (7). The melting range increases by 8°C during heat conditioning, and the crystal lattice dimensions, as measured by X-ray, decrease. The original condition can be restored by dissolution and subsequent precipitation or by melting and quenching the polymer. Sarel and Pohoryles make the assumption, based on the X-ray investigations, that the macromolecules of this polymer are folded in the crystallite structure.

The aliphatic polycarbonates have low intermolecular forces which cause correspondingly low melting ranges and high solubility in many organic solvents, such as methylene chloride, chloroform, benzene, acetone, and acetic acid. Alcohol, ether, and aliphatic hydrocarbons are nonsolvents for the aliphatic polycarbonates. Little has been reported on mechanical or electrical properties of aliphatic polycarbonates. Films and fibers from high molecular weight polycarbonates can be oriented by stretching.

Peterson (12) made films by solvent casting the polycarbonate from 1,6-hexanediol having an intrinsic viscosity of 0.57 dl/g measured in chloroform. These films were oriented in one direction by cold rolling. The tensile strength of the oriented film was 8290 psi, $\sim$ 580 kg/cm^2 (based on the original dimensions), in the direction of orientation and 4190 psi, $\sim$ 290 kg/cm^2, perpendicular to the direction of orientation. We made a polycarbonate from 1,6-hexanediol with a relative viscosity of 1.414, measured on a 0.5% solution in methylene chloride at 25°C. When this polycarbonate was solvent-cast from methylene chloride solution, we obtained a tensile strength of 3200 psi, 230 kg/cm^2, at an elongation of 305% on the unoriented film. These tensile strength values are still rather poor compared to other crystalline polymers. The polycarbonate from 2,2-dimethyl-1,3-propanediol solidifies from the melt to a viscoelastic polymer. Rubber elastic threads can be drawn from its melt.

Aliphatic polycarbonates are stable in a melt at temperatures above 200°C if alkaline or acidic impurities are not present. However, extremely small amounts of impurities, especially of alkaline reaction, cause a degradation and decomposition of the aliphatic polycarbonates at temperatures above 150°C. The reaction mechanism which can occur during this degradation depends on the particular polycarbonate, the amount of alkaline catalyst, the temperature, and the pressure. Carbon dioxide, unsaturated alcohols, cyclic ethers, polyethers, and cyclic monomeric and dimeric carbonates were isolated among the decomposition products, as well as some unknown volatile compounds. Some of the aliphatic polycarbonates are completely degraded, whereas others form cross-linked, insoluble, and infusible products or polyethers.

Carothers and van Natta (10) isolated allyl alcohol and some higher boiling unsaturated compounds when they degraded polytrimethylene-glycolcarbonate at atmospheric pressure and 210°C. The same polymer splits off cyclic trimethyleneglycolcarbonate if heated at 10 mm Hg. When polytetramethyleneglycolcarbonate was heated to 300–325° C under high vacuum, they obtained the dimeric cyclic tetramethyleneglycolcarbonate besides unknown unsaturated compounds. Hill and Carothers (10) heated aliphatic polycarbonates in a high vacuum under conditions of simplified molecular distillation. Under these conditions they were able to isolate the monomeric and dimeric cyclic carbonates from the decomposition products. (See Table III-2.)

TABLE III-2

Preparation of Cyclic Carbonates by
Depolymerization of Aliphatic Polycarbonates

Polycarbonate	Depolymerization products		
$H\left[-O(-CH_2)_n-O-\overset{\overset{O}{\parallel}}{C}\right]_x$ $n =$	$\underset{(CH_2)_n}{\overset{O}{\diagup}}\ \underset{O}{\overset{C=O}{\diagdown}}$ Monomeric cyclic carbonate	$O-\overset{\overset{O}{\parallel}}{C}-O$ $(CH_2)_n\ (CH_2)_n$ $O-\underset{\underset{O}{\parallel}}{C}-O$ Dimeric cyclic carbonate	Other identified decomposition products
4		+	Tetrahydrofuran
5		+	
6		+	
7		+	
8	+	+	
9	+	+	
10	+	+	
12	+	+	
13	+		
14	+		
18	+		

Hill (17) isolated polydecamethylene oxide in the residues of the thermal decomposition of polydecamethylene glycolcarbonate in a low vacuum. The polydecamethylene oxide also contained some decene-9-ol-1. This unsaturated alcohol was found, besides the 13- and 26-membered cyclic carbonates, in the volatile decomposition products. 2,2-Disubstituted 1,3-propanediol derivatives, such as 2,2-dimethyl- or 2-methyl-2-n-propyl-1,3-propanediol, form the corresponding cyclic carbonates easily and in good yield when heated at atmospheric pressure (7).

Aliphatic polycarbonates have not found any technical significance as intermediates for the preparation of crosslinked molded articles or in the area of films, fibers, or thermoplastics. This result is due primarily to their low melting points, their high solubility, their hydrophylic nature, and their oftentimes low thermal stability.

2. ALIPHATIC-AROMATIC POLYCARBONATES

In addition to the purely aliphatic dihydroxy compounds, Carothers and van Natta (10) also used p-xylylene glycol as an aliphatic-aromatic dihydroxy compound to prepare a polycarbonate. During the transesterification of p-xylylene glycol with diethyl carbonate under the catalytic effect of the sodium alcoholate of the p-xylylene glycol, which was produced in the reaction mixture, they obtained an obviously inhomogeneous microcrystalline polyester of low molecular weight. This product was only partially soluble in ethylene chloride. The soluble portion melted at 137–138°C and the insoluble portion melted at 177–185°C. Reynolds and Van Den Berghe (18) were able to show that the preparation of high molecular weight polycarbonates from p-xylylene glycol in the presence of a strongly alkaline transesterification catalyst is impossible because the benzyl-carbonic acid ester groups are not stable under these conditions. Experiments showed that they could obtain dibenzylether, benzaldehyde, toluene, and carbon dioxide if they heated benzyl-ethyl carbonate in the presence of lithium-aluminium ethylate to temperatures of approximately 250°C. II-25. They prepared high molecular weight polycarbonates of p-xylylene glycol by polycondensation of the bisalkyl or bisaryl carbonate of p-xylylene glycol by splitting off dialkyl or diaryl carbonate in the presence of titanium catalysts, such as tetrabutyl titanate, titanium tetrachloride or titanium tetrabromide (section III, 1, A, 4). At temperatures up to 250°C these catalysts only slightly degrade the p-xylylene glycol bisalkyl carbonate or the polycarbonates formed.

Catalysts of the type $M(OR)_2 \cdot Ti(OR)_4$, where $M = Mg, Ca, Sr; R =$

(III-25)

$$\text{C}_6\text{H}_5-\text{CH}_2-\text{O}-\overset{\text{O}}{\overset{\|}{\text{C}}}-\text{O}-\text{CH}_2-\text{CH}_3 \xrightarrow{\text{LiAl(OC}_2\text{H}_5)_4}$$

$$\text{C}_6\text{H}_5-\text{CH}_2-\text{O}-\overset{\text{O}}{\overset{\|}{\text{C}}}-\text{O}-\text{CH}_2-\text{C}_6\text{H}_5 \;+\; \text{C}_2\text{H}_5-\text{O}-\overset{\text{O}}{\overset{\|}{\text{C}}}-\text{O}-\text{C}_2\text{H}_5$$

$$\downarrow$$

$$\text{C}_6\text{H}_5-\text{CH}_2-\text{O}-\text{CH}_2-\text{C}_6\text{H}_5 \;+\; \text{CO}_2$$

$$\downarrow$$

$$\text{C}_6\text{H}_5-\overset{\text{O}}{\overset{\nwarrow}{\text{C}}}_\text{H} \;+\; \text{C}_6\text{H}_5-\text{CH}_3$$

alkyl C_1-C_{18}, can also be used for this polycondensation reaction (19). The p-xylylene glycol bisalkyl or bisaryl carbonates used as the raw material for this condensation can be made, for example, by reaction of p-xylylene glycol with alkyl or aryl chlorocarbonic acid esters in pyridine.

The same procedure was used for a number of other aliphatic-aromatic dihydroxy compounds to form their corresponding polycarbonates. (See Table III-3.)

TABLE III-3
Polycarbonates Made by Polycondensation of Bisalkyl or
Bisaryl Carbonates of Aliphatic-Aromatic Dihydroxy Compounds

Polycarbonates from	Intrinsic viscosity (phenol: tetrachloroethane 60:40) [dl/g]	Melting range [°C]	Properties	References
HO—CH$_2$—C$_6$H$_4$—CH$_2$—OH	0.62	239	High tendency to crystallize, white, porcelainlike	(18)
HO(—CH$_2$)$_2$—C$_6$H$_4$—(CH$_2$—)$_2$OH	0.87	215	"	(19) (20)
HO—CH$_2$—C$_6$H$_4$—C$_6$H$_4$—CH$_2$—OH	Insoluble	260	"	(19) (21)
HO(—CH$_2$)$_2$—C$_6$H$_4$—C$_6$H$_4$—(CH$_2$—)$_2$OH	0.79	245	"	(19) (22)

Reynolds and Van Den Berghe (23) obtained high molecular aliphatic-aromatic polycarbonates of the type H-$(O$-CH_2-CH_2-O-R-O-CH_2-CH_2-

$$O$$
$$\|$$

O-C-$)_x$ (R representing an aromatic residue) by polycondensation of bisaryl or bisalkyl carbonates of the bis-hydroxyethyl ethers of aromatic dihydroxy compounds using the abovementioned catalysts. Polycarbonates of this kind were also made by Caldwell (24) by transesterification of bis-hydroxyethyl ethers of aromatic dihydroxy compounds with dialkyl carbonates in the presence of bimetal complexes of magnesium, calcium, or strontium with aluminium or titanium of the general formula

$$M[Al(OR)_4]_2 \quad M[H\ Ti(OR)_6]_2 \quad \text{and} \quad M[Ti(OR)_6]$$

where M = Ca, Sr, Mg; R = alkyl with 1–6 carbon atoms.

The best procedure to produce these polycarbonates is the transesterification of bis-hydroxyalkyl ethers of aromatic dihydroxy compounds with diaryl carbonates (25). Using this procedure, we do not need a transesterification catalyst (section III, 1, A, *3*).

High molecular weight polycarbonates can also be obtained by phosgenation of solutions of bis-hydroxyalkyl ethers of aromatic dihydroxy compounds in the presence of pyridine (section III, 1, A, *1*) (24). (See Table III-4.)

Little is known about the properties of aliphatic-aromatic polycarbonates. The melting range is increased considerably compared to the aliphatic polycarbonates due to the aromatic rings. However, it is still considerably lower than the melting range of aromatic polycarbonates. Thus polycarbonate from hydroquinone melts above 300°C with decomposition. The addition of one —CH_2-group between the aromatic ring and the OH-group decreases the melting range of the polycarbonate to 239°C. If a —CH_2—CH_2-group is added between the OH-group and the aromatic ring, the melting point is lowered to 215°C, and a —O—CH_2—CH_2-group will lower the melting point to 144°C. A similar dependency of the melting range of aliphatic-aromatic polycarbonates on the particular dihydroxy compound can also be shown in polycarbonates based on diphenyl derivatives.

The high melting range of the polycarbonate from hydroquinone is caused by the intermolecular forces between the aromatic rings, the high degree of crystallinity of this polymer, and the decreased mobility of the polymer backbone.

The aliphatic-aromatic polycarbonates, which have the same degree of crystallinity as the corresponding aromatic polycarbonates, melt at considerably lower temperatures. This is caused primarily by the increased mobility of the macromolecules due to the aliphatic groups. Many of the aliphatic-aromatic polycarbonates investigated showed a great tendency to crystallize. From the melt they usually solidify to an opaque and, in many cases, brittle microcrystalline mass. Fibers which can be oriented by stretching can be pulled from their respective melts. The orientation is fixed by the high degree of crystallinity. The aliphatic-aromatic polycarbonates show a poor stability at high temperatures, especially in the presence of alkaline compounds. Experiments with benzyl-ethyl carbonate make it probable that polycarbonates containing

the

$$-\langle\bigcirc\rangle-CH_2-O-\overset{\overset{\displaystyle O}{\|}}{C}-O-$$

group will thermally decompose to CO_2, polyethers, aromatic hydrocarbons, and resins which are formed by secondary reactions of aldehyde groups. The thermal degradation of phenyl-ethyl-alkyl carbonate yields CO_2, alkyl alcohol, and styrene (19). This explains the formation of crosslinked polymers in the thermal degradation of polycarbonate containing the group

$$-\langle\bigcirc\rangle-CH_2-CH_2-O-\overset{\overset{\displaystyle O}{\|}}{C}-O-$$

Crosslinking occurs by the polymerization of unsaturated decomposition products. Polycarbonates based on oxyalkylated aromatic dihydroxy compounds are comparable to aliphatic polycarbonates in their thermal stability. The highly crystalline aliphatic-aromatic polycarbonates are insoluble in the more common organic solvents. The aliphatic-aromatic polycarbonates have not found any practical application to date.

3. AROMATIC POLYCARBONATES

The definition "aromatic polycarbonates" is used to refer to polyesters of carbonic acid which are derived from dihydroxyl compounds in which the hydroxyl-groups are directly attached to an aromatic ring.

The first experiments for the preparation of aromatic polycarbonates were carried out in 1898 by Einhorn and in 1902 by Bischoff and Hedenstroem (Chapter II). The polyesters prepared, based on hydroquinone and resorcinol, showed such limited useful properties that for the next 50

TABLE III-4

Aliphatic-Aromatic Polycarbonates from Bis-Hydroxy Alkyl Ethers of Aromatic Dihydroxy Compounds

Polycarbonate from	Solution viscosity	Melting range [°C]	Properties	Reference
$HO(-CH_2)_2-O-$⟨benzene⟩$-O(-CH_2)_2-OH$	Inherent viscosity 0.61 [dl/g] (in phenol-tetra-chloroethane 60:40)	144–147	Viscoelastic, transparent	(24)
$HO(-CH_2)_2-O-$⟨tetrachlorobenzene Cl Cl / Cl Cl⟩$-O(-CH_2)_2-OH$	…	195–198	Viscoelastic, transparent	(25)
$HO(-CH_2)_2-O-$⟨biphenyl⟩$-O(-CH_2)_2-OH$	Intrinsic viscosity = 0.69 [dl/g] (phenol-tetra-chloroethane 60:40)	225	Highly crystalline, porcelainlike	(23) (24)
$HO(-CH_2)_2-O-$⟨naphthalene⟩$-O(-CH_2)_2-OH$	Viscosity number $Z_\eta = 56 \cdot 10^{-3}$ [l/g] (tetra-chloroethane 30°C)	200	Crystalline, opaque	(25)

Structure				
HO(—CH₂)₂—O—⟨C₆H₄⟩—C(CH₃)(CH₃)—⟨C₆H₄⟩—O(—CH₂)₂—OH	…	120–130	Soluble	(24) (26)
HO—CH—CH₂—O—⟨C₆H₄⟩—C(CH₃)(CH₃)—⟨C₆H₄⟩—O—CH₂—CH—OH (with CH₃ groups)	…	100–125	…	(26)
HO(—CH₂)₂—O—⟨C₆H₄⟩—C(=O)—⟨C₆H₄⟩—O(—CH₂)₂—OH	…	150–160	Viscoelastic	(24)
HO(—CH₂)₂—O—⟨C₆H₄⟩—S(=O)(=O)—⟨C₆H₄⟩—O(—CH₂)₂—OH	…	145–155	Viscoelastic	(24)

years aromatic polycarbonates were not mentioned in the technical or patent literature. Aromatic polycarbonates were recalled to the interest of the scientific world by a paper given by H. Schnell at the meeting of the *Gesellschaft Deutscher Chemiker* (German Chemical Society) in Hamburg on September 22, 1956. In this paper, titled *Polycarbonate, eine Gruppe neuartiger thermoplastischer Kunststoffe*, the exceptional properties of thermoplastic aromatic polycarbonates based on 4,4'-dihydroxydiaryl alkanes were disclosed (27).

4,4'-Dihydroxydiaryl alkanes are compounds of the general formula

$$HO-\underset{}{\bigcirc}-R-\underset{}{\bigcirc}-OH$$

R representing an aliphatic residue.

4,4'-Dihydroxydiaryl methane derivatives of the general formula

$$HO-\bigcirc-\overset{R_1}{\underset{R_2}{C}}-\bigcirc-OH$$

in which alkyl, aryl, or halogen substituents may be present on the aromatic ring and in which R_1 and R_2 representing H, alkyl, or aryl groups are easily accessible. Many of these aromatic dihydroxy compounds are obtainable without any difficulty by the reactions of carbonyl compounds, such as aldehydes and ketones, with phenols. The reaction product of acetone and phenol, 4,4'-dihydroxy-diphenyl-2,2-propane or 2,2-bis (4-hydroxyphenyl) propane, with the structural formula,

$$HO-\bigcirc-\overset{CH_3}{\underset{CH_3}{C}}-\bigcirc-OH$$

is the most important hydroxyl component for polycarbonates today. This compound is also known as bisphenol A.

The preparation of the 4,4'-dihydroxy-diphenyl alkanes, and other dihydroxy compounds suitable for the preparation of thermoplastic polycarbonates, such as 4,4'-dihydroxydiphenyl ethers or sulfides or sulfones, are treated in Chapter IV.

Since 1956 aromatic polycarbonates have been prepared in many universities and industrial laboratories all over the world. This work is reported in more than 300 patent applications, patents, and technical articles.

A. Preparation of Aromatic Polycarbonates

Aromatic polycarbonates cannot be prepared by the direct phosgenation of aromatic dihydroxy compounds. Aromatic dihydroxy compounds react with phosgene more slowly than do aliphatic dihydroxy compounds. In most cases a sufficient reaction velocity will be reached only at temperatures exceeding 150°C. But even at these temperatures, the passing of phosgene into solutions or melts of aromatic dihydroxy compounds does not result in high molecular weight polycarbonate. On the other hand the phosgenation of aromatic dihydroxy compounds in the presence of pyridine, the interfacial polycondensation of aqueous solutions of the alkali salts of aromatic dihydroxy compounds with a phosgene solution, as well as the transesterification of aromatic dihydroxy compounds with diaryl carbonates will produce high polymers.

Each of these processes is illustrated below, using bisphenol A as a starting material, because polycarbonate based on it, is commercially produced and the process for its preparation is described in the technical and patent literature.

1. Preparation of Aromatic Polycarbonates by Phosgenation of Aromatic Dihydroxy Compounds in the Presence of Pyridine

The saltlike adducts (III-10, III-11) formed from pyridine and phosgene or aromatic chlorocarbonates are substantially more reactive with aromatic hydroxy compounds than the corresponding carbonic acid derivatives themselves.

The phosgenation of aromatic dihydroxy compounds in the presence of pyridine, as described previously in the preparation of aliphatic polycarbonates, must take place in the absence of water and in the presence of at least two moles of pyridine per mole of phosgene. Under these conditions, at room temperatures or below, polycarbonate is formed as shown in formula III-26. The reaction is so rapid that the process can be carried out continuously.

A prerequisite for the preparation of high molecular weight polycarbonate with favorable properties in accordance with this process is the solubility of the polycarbonate formed in pyridine. Since in the reaction two moles of pyridine hydrochloride are formed for each mole of aromatic dihydroxy compound, it is necessary to use a large excess of pyridine to maintain the reaction in a liquid phase.

(III-26) x HO—⟨ ⟩—C(CH₃)(CH₃)—⟨ ⟩—OH + x COCl₂ $\xrightarrow{\text{Pyridine}}$

$$H\left[-O-\bigcirc-\underset{CH_3}{\overset{CH_3}{C}}-\bigcirc-O-\overset{O}{\overset{\|}{C}}-\right]_x + 2x\bigcirc N\cdot HCl$$

With a view to the following isolation and purification of the poly-carbonate, it is more advantageous to use only sufficient pyridine to react with the hydrogen chloride formed during the phosgenation and to use such a quantity of a nonreactive solvent in which the polycarbonate formed is soluble that the polyester remains as a viscous solution (28) after the separation of the pyridine and pyridine hydrochloride is ac-complished. The preparation of polycarbonate from bisphenol A by this process can be carried out as follows:

> Into a solution of 114 g of bisphenol A in 120 g of anhydrous pyridine and 515 g of dry methylene chloride (methanol free) introduce at 25°C 48 g of gaseous phosgene with agitation and cooling within 90 minutes. Near the end of the addition the solution will become viscous. Thin the solution with an additional 550 g of dry methylene chloride and within about 30 minutes add a solution of 3 g of phosgene in 40 g of methylene chloride dropwise. After one hour wash the reaction mixture first with 10% hydrochloric acid and then with water until chloride ions can no longer be detected in the wash water. Precipitate the re-sulting viscous solution of the polycarbonate in methylene chloride by the addition of petroleum ether with agitation. Filter the finely divided white precipitate and dry it at 120°C under vacuum. The relative viscosity, η_{rel}, of the polymer will be 1.35, measured as a 0.5% solution in methylene chloride at 20°C.

This process can be used for the preparation of all polycarbonates soluble in methylene chloride. This applies to most of the polycarbonates based on 4,4'-dihydroxy-diphenyl methane derivatives.

The molecular weight of the resulting polycarbonate is influenced principally by the reaction temperature, the quantity of pyridine used, the rate of phosgene addition, and the presence of chain terminators. An excess of pyridine and a slow addition of the last 5 to 10% of the phosgene favor reaching higher molecular weights (29).

Instead of methylene chloride, other nonreactive solvents in which the resultant polycarbonate is soluble can be used; for some products benzene and toluene have been used.

The polycarbonate can be recovered from the solutions by methods usual in polymer chemistry: e.g., by evaporation of the solvent or by precipitation with nonsolvents.

The General Electric Company has developed a commercial method for the preparation of polycarbonates based on bisphenol A, using phosgenation in the presence of pyridine. A plant for the preparation of 2500 metric tons per year (5 million lb per year) has been erected in Mt. Vernon, Indiana, and is in commercial operation (30).

Figure III-1 shows the simplified process flow diagram for this plant, and an outline of the process is indicated below.

A solution of bisphenol A in a mixture of inert solvent and pyridine is phosgenated. A suitable solvent is, for example, methylene chloride. The solution of the polymer is washed with dilute hydrochloric acid, by which the excess pyridine is converted to the hydrochloride and transferred into the aqueous phase together with the pyridine hydrochloride formed during the reaction. The phases are separated. The polymer is separated from the organic solvent by agitating the solution with a precipitant, such as the aliphatic hydrocarbons. The polyester is obtained in the form of a white powder, which is filtered off and dried.

The solvent-precipitant solution from the filtration and drying is collected and the solvent and nonsolvent are separated by distillation and returned to the process. The polycarbonate powder is extruded and pelletized.

The aqueous phase is neutralized with an equimolar quantity of caustic soda. The mixture is stripped first of the solvent and then of the pyridine-water azeotrope.

The pyridine-water azeotrope is broken and pyridine is redistilled to the required purity. It is returned to the process, as is the recovered solvent. The advantage of this process is that the polycondensation is carried out in a homogeneous liquid phase at low temperatures. It is burdened by the utilization of pyridine (odor, cost), as well as by the use of solvent and a precipitant (nonsolvent) which have to be separated and recovered in an anhydrous form.

2. Preparation of Aromatic Polycarbonates by Interfacial Polycondensation

This section describes the preparation of aromatic polycarbonates by the reaction of aqueous alkaline solutions of aromatic dihydroxy com-

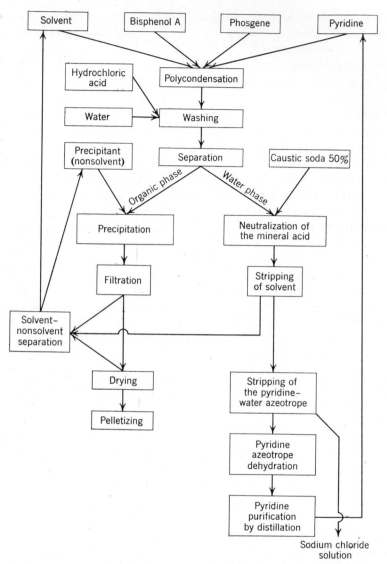

Fig. III-1. Preparation of polycarbonate from bisphenol A by phosgenation in the presence of pyridine.

pounds with phosgene or with bis-chlorocarbonic acid esters of aromatic dihydroxy compounds in the presence of inert solvents.

An undesirable side reaction, which will be present in aqueous systems, is the reaction of phosgene with water. Phosgene is hydrolyzed very rapidly in water to hydrochloric acid and carbon dioxide in a pseudomonomolecular reaction, possibly following an addition-elimination reaction mechanism. The reaction rate constant of the hydrolysis of phosgene in a solvent mixture of water/acetone ($x_{H_2O} = 0.048$) at $-50°C$ is $K_{H_2O} = 2.36 \times 10^{-2}[\text{sec}^{-1}]$ (31).

Phosgene is also rapidly hydrolyzed in two-phase mixtures of phosgene and water, or a mixture of phosgene solutions in inert solvents and water, or by passing gaseous phosgene through water. It is therefore not possible to obtain aliphatic mono- or dichlorocarbonic acid esters, dialkyl carbonates, or polycarbonates by reaction of phosgene directly with aliphatic mono- or dihydroxy compounds in the presence of water.

The reaction of phosgene with alkali phenolates, on the other hand, is very rapid. Thus the introduction of phosgene into aqueous solutions of the alkali salts of aromatic hydroxy compounds forms aryl chlorocarbonic esters at room temperature or below. The aryl chlorocarbonic esters react much more slowly with additional alkali phenolates, so that to obtain reasonable rates for this reaction temperatures up to about 80°C are required. Phosgene, as well as aryl chlorocarbonic acid esters, are partially hydrolyzed under these conditions. Consequently, to obtain high yields of diaryl carbonates, an excess of phosgene and caustic is necessary.

When phosgene is passed into aqueous solutions of the alkali salts of aromatic dihydroxy compounds, primary chlorocarbonic acid esters are formed, which separate from the reaction mixture. These partially react further to build low molecular weight polycarbonate with chlorocarbonic acid end groups, which, like phosgene, are partially hydrolyzed under the reaction conditions.

As the end product of this reaction low molecular weight, halogen containing polyesters are obtained in which a part of the chlorocarbonic acid ester end groups are removed from further reaction and hydrolysis by inclusion into the hydrophobic polyester.

In the preparation of diaryl carbonates the hydrolysis of phosgene and chlorocarbonic acid ester groups can be suppressed by introducing the phosgene into a two-phase mixture of an aqueous alkaline solution of an aromatic hydroxy compound and an inert, water-insoluble solvent. The hydrolysis can also be suppressed by reacting a solution of phosgene in an inert solvent with the phenolate solution. In this manner diaryl carbonates can be prepared in good yields.

By the utilization of this technique with aromatic dihydroxy compounds, Einhorn (32) obtained a low molecular weight, chlorine-containing polycarbonate by shaking a phosgene solution in toluene with aqueous alkaline solutions of resorcinol and hydroquinone.

By the introduction of phosgene into an agitated, two-phase mixture of xylene isomers and an alkaline solution of 4,4'-dihydroxy-diphenyl-2,2-propane in aqueous caustic soda solution at room temperature, Schnell and co-workers obtained for the first time high molecular weight, thermoplastic aromatic polycarbonates (27,28). During the reaction the polyester separated in the form of white swollen particles. Even after extended treatment in alkaline medium at temperatures up to 100°C it was not possible to get the polyester completely free from chlorine. Apparently some polymer with chlorocarbonic ester end groups was occluded by the hydrophobic polycarbonate, the chlorocarbonate groups thus being pro-

(III-27)

tected from hydrolysis. It was also found to be difficult to remove all the inorganic salts formed during the reaction.

In many cases the polymer particles which separate are not homogeneous. The low molecular weight polycarbonate, which separates from the reaction mixture first, is coated with a layer of high molecular weight polyester formed during the later stage of the reaction. This coating prevents further reaction of the low molecular weight nucleus of the particle. This results in products with a molecular-weight distribution function with two maxima (27). Test specimens made from these polycarbonates show good mechanical properties only at relatively high molecular weight. Films cast from solutions have a characteristic crispy feel, similar to thin aluminum foil.

Improved product quality results when an inert solvent is utilized in which both the phosgene and the polycarbonate produced are soluble. Upon addition of phosgene to an agitated two-phase mixture of such a solvent and the alkaline solution of the sodium salt of the aromatic dihydroxy compound at room temperature, solutions of relatively low viscosity of low molecular weight polycarbonates bearing chlorocarbonic ester end groups are first formed. These will slowly convert to high molecular weight products on continued agitation. The reaction can be accelerated by elevated temperature (27,28). Depending on the quantity of inert solvent used, the polycarbonate separates either as a heavy dough or as a viscous solution.

In this process chlorinated aliphatic compounds, e.g., methylene chloride, are especially suitable as solvents for the preparation of polycarbonates based on 4,4'-dihydroxy-diphenyl methane derivatives.

Using reaction temperatures of about 0 to 40°C, polycarbonates with molecular weights up to 200,000 may be prepared simply by this process. Lower molecular weight products can be reproducibly prepared by the use of chain terminators, e.g., aromatic monohydroxy compounds.

Since alkali salts of aromatic dihydroxy compounds are easily oxidized to colored compounds in alkaline media, it is advisable to exclude oxygen during the polycondensation and to use reducing agents such as sodium dithionite (28).

Strong alkalies, such as sodium or potassium hydroxide, are best suited to carry out this reaction. It is advantageous to maintain a pH value in excess of 10 during the course of the polycondensation by the use of excess alkali (28,29,33). The total alkali can be added at the beginning of the polycondensation, or a part can be initially placed in the reaction vessel and the remainder added during the phosgenation (28,29,34). If weak alkalies, such as sodium carbonate or sodium bicarbonate are utilized in the polycondensation, only low molecular weight polycarbonates containing chlorocarbonic acid ester end groups are formed. Under these conditions the reaction of the chlorocarbonic esters with the sodium salts of aromatic dihydroxy compounds proceeds very slowly (35).

The polycondensation is an exothermic reaction. It is advisable to remove the heat of reaction by cooling. The resulting polycarbonate solutions are washed free of electrolytes with water, and the polyester is separated by methods customary in plastic technology, for example, by the evaporation of the solvent (section III, 3, A, 3).

The process described is not particularly suitable for a continuous polycondensation. Although low molecular weight polycarbonates with chlorocarbonic ester groups are formed rapidly, the continuing reaction of this product with the alkali salts of aromatic dihydroxy compounds leading to high molecular weight product proceeds slowly at temperatures up to 40°C. It is not advisable to carry out the reaction at higher temperatures, since this favors the hydrolysis of the phosgene and the chlorocarbonic acid ester groups.

Bottenbruch and Schnell (36) found that small quantities of tertiary amines, such as triethylamine, N,N-dimethyl-cyclohexylamine, or quaternary ammonium bases, such as tetramethyl ammonium hydroxide and triethyl benzyl ammonium hydroxide, greatly accelerate the interfacial polycondensation of alkali salts of aromatic dihydroxy compounds with phosgene. This acceleration of the reaction is especially pronounced for the reaction of chlorocarbonic acid esters with the alkali salts of aromatic dihydroxy compounds and with low molecular weight polycarbonates. For this reason the catalysts can be added after the first stage of the condensation, which is rapid without the use of catalysts and in which polycarbonate with chlorocarbonic acid ester end groups is formed.

Considering the instability in water of the saltlike adducts of phosgene and chlorocarbonic acid esters with tertiary amines (section III, 1, A, *1*), the catalytic action of these amines on the interfacial polycondensation is surprising. It can be explained only by the formation in the organic phase of a reactive, saltlike adduct of the amine and the chlorocarbonic acid ester of the aromatic dihydroxy compound or a growing polycarbonate chain. The reaction of these complexes with the alkali salt of the

(III–28)

$$\cdots-O-\bigcirc-\underset{\underset{CH_3}{|}}{\overset{\overset{CH_3}{|}}{C}}-\bigcirc-O-\overset{\overset{O}{||}}{C}-Cl \ + \ N\underset{R}{\overset{R}{<}} \longrightarrow$$

$$\left[\cdots-O-\bigcirc-\underset{\underset{CH_3}{|}}{\overset{\overset{CH_3}{|}}{C}}-\bigcirc-O-\overset{\overset{O}{||}}{C}-\overset{(+)}{N}\underset{R}{\overset{R}{<}}\right]Cl^{(-)}$$

aromatic dihydroxy compound or with a polycarbonate chain at the interface is promoted to such an extent that hydrolysis becomes secondary. By this reaction a carbonic acid ester group and sodium chloride

(III–29)

$$\left[\cdots-O-\bigcirc-\underset{\underset{CH_3}{|}}{\overset{\overset{CH_3}{|}}{C}}-\bigcirc-O-\overset{\overset{O}{||}}{C}-\overset{(+)}{N}\underset{R}{\overset{R}{<}}\right]Cl^{(-)} \ + \ NaO-\bigcirc-\underset{\underset{CH_3}{|}}{\overset{\overset{CH_3}{|}}{C}}-\bigcirc-O\cdots$$

$$\xrightarrow[\text{H}_2\text{O}]{\text{NaOH}} \ \cdots-O-\bigcirc-\underset{\underset{CH_3}{|}}{\overset{\overset{CH_3}{|}}{C}}-\bigcirc-O-\overset{\overset{O}{||}}{C}-O-\bigcirc-\underset{\underset{CH_3}{|}}{\overset{\overset{CH_3}{|}}{C}}-\bigcirc-O\cdots$$

$$+ \ R-\underset{R}{\overset{R}{N}} \ + \ NaCl$$

are formed and the amine is liberated. The amine returns to the organic phase and again forms a reactive adduct with a chlorocarbonic acid ester group. Quaternary phosphonium, quaternary arsenium, or tertiary sulfonium compounds are also said to be efficient as catalysts (37).

Under the catalytic action of tertiary amines or quaternary ammonium bases the interfacial polycondensation just described can be carried out at such a rate at room or lower temperatures that the reaction can be made continuous (38).

The preparation of a polycarbonate from bisphenol A by this process can be carried out as follows:

454 g of 4,4'-dihydroxy-diphenyl-2,2-propane and 9.5 of *p-tert*-butyl phenol are suspended in 1.5 liters of water. In a three-neck flask equipped with good agitation and a gas addition dip tube oxygen is removed from the mixture by blowing nitrogen through it while agitating for 15 minutes. Then 365 g of 45% sodium hydroxide and 1000 g of methylene chloride are added. The mixture is cooled to 25°C by external cooling. While maintaining this temperature by cooling, 236.5 g of gaseous phosgene are added evenly over a 120-minute period. An additional 75 g each of 45% sodium hydroxide solution are added 15 and 30 minutes after the phosgene addition has been started. To the resulting low-viscosity solution of low molecular weight polycarbonate bearing chlorocarbonic acid ester end groups, 1.6 g of triethyl amine is added and the mixture is agitated for an additional 15 minutes. Now a highly viscous solution of high molecular weight polycarbonate is formed. By the addition of more methylene chloride the viscosity of the solution is adjusted to the desired level, the aqueous phase is separated, and the organic phase is washed with water until free of salt and alkali. From the resulting solution the polycarbonate is recovered (section III, 3, A, *3*) and dried for 24 hours at 120°C and 30 mm Hg.

The polycarbonate has a relative viscosity of about 1.32, measured as 0.5% solution in methylene chloride at 20°C.

In the preparation of polycarbonates with the help of amine-catalyzed interfacial polycondensation, the chlorocarbonic acid ester end groups remaining at the end of the reaction are rapidly hydrolyzed, so that chlorine-free polycarbonates are obtained.

In the uncatalyzed polycondensation reaction, on the other hand, a postreaction time is required in alkaline medium to hydrolyze the chlorocarbonic acid ester end groups completely. It has been proposed to shorten this postreaction time by the addition of small quantities of solutions of certain amines after the separation of the alkaline salt solution (39). Amines suggested include pyridine, quinoline, or other aromatic amines, such as N-methyl aniline and toluidine.

The interfacial polycondensation process can be carried out as shown in the simplified flow diagram (Fig. III-2):

The attractive features of the process are the simplicity of the reaction at low temperatures, the use of only one organic solvent, and the ability to prepare a condensation polymer of very high molecular weight, up to 200,000. Complete removal of the electrolytes from the polymer solution by washing is a difficulty from a technological standpoint.

The molecular weight distribution function of the polymer has an influence on the physical properties obtained. The interfacial polycondensation process produces a polycarbonate with normal distribution. The molecular weight distribution can be narrowed, with a corresponding

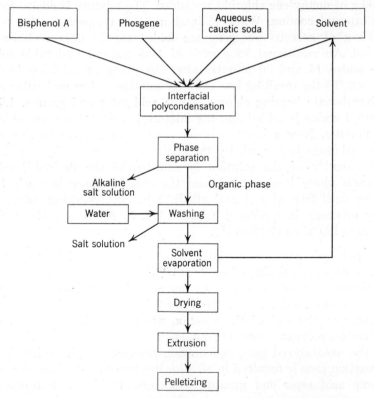

Fig. III-2. Preparation of polycarbonate from bisphenol A by interfacial polycondensation (37).

improvement in properties (Chapter V), if a polyester is prepared with higher than desired molecular weight and this is then degraded thermally or by hydrolysis, alcoholysis, or phenolysis to the molecular weight desired (40).

Instead of the use of phosgene in interfacial polycondensation, the bis-chlorocarbonic esters or aromatic dihydroxy compound as such can, of course, be used (27). Compounds which have the capability to react as phosgene or bis-chlorocarbonic acid esters under the reaction conditions can also be used (9,41). Such compounds are, for example, chlorocarbonic acid trichloromethyl ester (di-phosgene), bis-trichloromethyl carbonate, or bis-trichloromethyl carbonates of aromatic dihydroxy compounds.

The interfacial polycondensation has also been used recently for the preparation of aromatic polyesters from 4,4'-dihydroxy-diphenyl alkanes and acid chlorides of aliphatic and aromatic dicarboxylic acids (42).

An interesting observation was made by F. Schimke (43). If the solution of a polycarbonate from bisphenol A in methylene chloride is emulsified in aqueous caustic soda solution, the chains will grow, accelerated by amine catalysts, such as tetramethyl ammonium bromide. Bisphenol A is split off simultaneously.

Schimke assumes that the polycarbonate is primarily hydrolyzed, that the terminal

$$-O-\overset{\overset{\text{O}}{\|}}{C}-OH$$

group formed reacts very quickly with the corresponding terminal group of another macromolecule, and that a new carbonate group is formed and the chain extended.

(III-30)

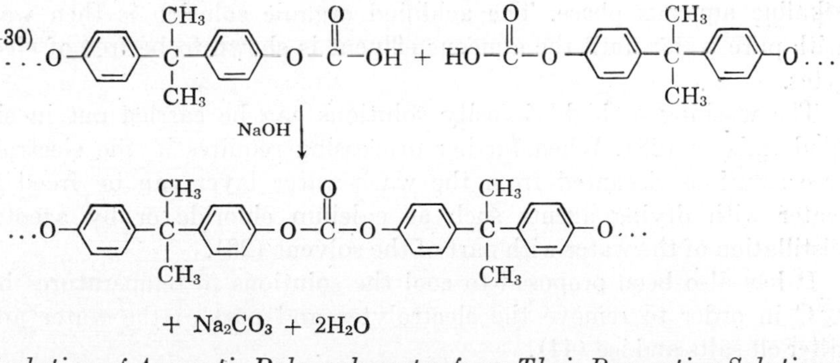

+ Na$_2$CO$_3$ + 2H$_2$O

3. Isolation of Aromatic Polycarbonates from Their Respective Solutions

The preparation of polycarbonates as solutions in an organic solvent has been discussed in the preceding pages (section III, 3, A, 1 and 2).

This section describes the purification and isolation from solution of the solid polycarbonate in a form suitable for thermoplastic processing. Obviously, the methods are intended for use only with thermoplastic polycarbonates soluble in suitable solvents such as methylene chloride.

Nearly all the finishing processes described apply specifically to the soluble, crystallizable polycarbonate based on bisphenol A but are also applicable to other soluble aromatic polycarbonates, especially those based on 4,4'-dihydroxy-diphenyl methane derivatives.

Processes utilizing the property of highly concentrated solutions to form gels cannot be used for polycarbonates with a very low tendency to crystallization. An important factor for such processes is the required capability of the polycarbonates to crystallize.

The solutions obtained by the phosgenation of aromatic dihydroxy compounds in the presence of pyridine and solvents, as well as those obtained by interfacial polycondensation, have varying viscosities, depending on the concentration of the solvent and the molecular weight of the polycarbonate. Highly concentrated solutions have the consistency of a viscous dough at room temperature.

Before the polymer is recovered from the solution all impurities obviously should be eliminated. For example, all electrolytes must be completely washed out of these solutions before further processing. For this reason, it is advisable to start the washing procedure with an aqueous solution of a mineral acid. In the pyridine process this acid wash converts the excess pyridine into the corresponding water-soluble salt. In the interfacial condensation process the acid serves to neutralize the residual alkalinity remaining in the organic phase after the separation of the alkaline aqueous phase. The acidified organic solution is then washed with pure water until the aqueous effluent is shown to be free of electrolytes.

The washing of high-viscosity solutions can be carried out in sigma blade mixers (28). When further processing requires it, the electrolyte-free solutions decanted from the wash-water layer can be freed from water with drying agents such as calcium chloride or by azeotropic distillation of the water with part of the solvent (28).

It has also been proposed to cool the solutions to temperatures below 0°C in order to remove the electrolytes and part of the water and to filter off salts and ice (44).

The polycarbonate solutions, free of electrolytes and water, can be utilized directly for the preparation of films or fibers after adjustment to the required viscosity, either by distillative removal of the excess solvent or by the addition of solvent. In most cases, however, it is necessary to recover the polyester from the solution in a form suitable for thermoplastic processing. This can be done through the utilization of extruders of proper design, in which the solvent is continuously evaporated from the solution and the polycarbonate is recovered as a melt (38, 45).

The polycarbonate is extruded as a rod or ribbon and is chopped into pellets. Since the melt of macromolecular substances tenaciously retains small quantities of organic solvents, it is not simple to remove the last traces of solvent by this method.

Another possibility is the precipitation of polycarbonate from its solutions by a nonsolvent, such as methanol (29), isopropanol (33), or aliphatic hydrocarbons (46). The precipitant is added to the vigorously agitated solution, whereby the polycarbonates separate in crystalline form as a fine powder which is filtered off and dried. The addition of polycarbonate powder to agitated solutions of polycarbonate, into which precipitant had been mixed until the cloud point was reached, accelerates the formation of solid, nonsticking polycarbonate powder on the addition of more precipitant (46). At suitable particle size these powdery polycarbonates can be utilized for special processing methods, such as centrifugal sintering or flame coating. In most cases it is necessary to extrude the powder to form a rod or ribbon to be cut into suitable pellets.

The precipitation process can be used only for crystallizable polycarbonates, as for example, polycarbonate based on bisphenol A. Polycarbonates with limited crystallization tendency form a swollen liquid phase upon the addition of precipitant, which is not suitable for further processing.

Even solutions of crystallizable polycarbonate can be converted into a swollen, rubberlike sol by rapid addition of the precipitant. On long standing at room temperature, or a shorter time at elevated temperature, these sols will form a solid, friable gel. In this form they can be mechanically reduced in size and the polycarbonate recovered as pellets by removal of the solvent by drying (47).

It is also possible to inject the polycarbonate solution into water or an organic precipitant at elevated temperatures, in which case the polycarbonate is recovered in fluffy small particles (48). For further pressing, the polycarbonate must be dried, densified, and extruded into pellet form.

The polycarbonate from bisphenol A is said to be recovered from solutions in methylene chloride in powder form as well if such solutions, after addition of at least 2 ml of xylene per g of polycarbonate, are mixed with water and if the organic solvents are then distilled off (49).

Another process for the separation from solutions of crystallizable, soluble polycarbonate, such as polycarbonate from bisphenol A, consists of the use of only so much solvent during the preparation that a highly concentrated, high-viscosity solution results. After washing and aging, this "dough" becomes a solid, friable gel, which can easily be reduced in size by mechanical means. The solvent can be removed from the granules either by direct means of evaporation of solvent or by stripping the solvent by boiling the granules in water and drying them. In this manner a powder with high bulk density is obtained (50).

A special method of interfacial polycondensation makes it possible to obtain the polycarbonate directly in the form of solid, discrete particles. In this process (section III, 3, A, *2*) the polycarbonate is first formed in the agitated reaction mixture as a dispersion of small droplets in the aqueous alkaline solution. During the polycondensation the disperse organic phase normally combines into a viscous solution. This coagulation of the disperse phase can be prevented by the addition of emulsifying and dispersing agents, such as fatty alcohol sulfates, polyvinyl alcohol, calcium oxide, and magnesium oxide. After the end of the polycondensation the droplets are partially solidified either by evaporation of a part of the solvent or by the addition of nonsolvents, so that they can be removed by filtration and washed. After drying, spherical particles, similar to those produced in the bead polymerization of vinyl compounds, are obtained. The diameter of these particles can be varied between wide limits, depnding on processing conditions (51).

4. Preparation of Aromatic Polycarbonates by Transesterification

The phosgenation of aromatic dihydroxy compounds in the presence of pyridine, as well as the interfacial polycondensation, results in products of useful mechanical properties only when the polycarbonate thus prepared is soluble in some inert organic solvent. The transesterification process can be applied for all aromatic polycarbonates, which can be melted below their decomposition temperature.

The transesterification of aromatic dihydroxy compounds with dialkyl carbonates is slow, even at temperatures higher than 200°C and in the presence of strongly alkaline transesterification catalysts such as sodium methoxide. When the temperature is sufficiently high and the catalyst is concentrated enough to give a practical rate of transesterification, part of the dialkyl carbonate and part of the polycarbonate formed are decomposed. For this reason this route is not technically feasible for the preparation of useful high molecular weight polycarbonates. The proposed transesterification of aromatic dihydroxy compounds with bis-lactic acid ester carbonate does not behave significantly better than the dialkyl carbonates (52).

In the absence of catalysts, the transesterification of aromatic dihydroxy compounds with diaryl carbonates at temperatures up to 280°C proceeds slowly, accompanied by the formation of volatile aromatic hydroxy compounds. Although the transesterification is only slightly accelerated by acid catalysts, it is accelerated markedly by basic catalysts (27,28). The variously described transesterifications of aromatic dihydroxy compounds with diphenyl carbonate, reportedly without the use of catalyst (53,54), were probably based on the accelerating action of alkaline impurity contained in the starting materials.

Theoretically, the preparation of aromatic polycarbonate by means of the transesterification process utilizes equimolar quantities of reagents as follows:

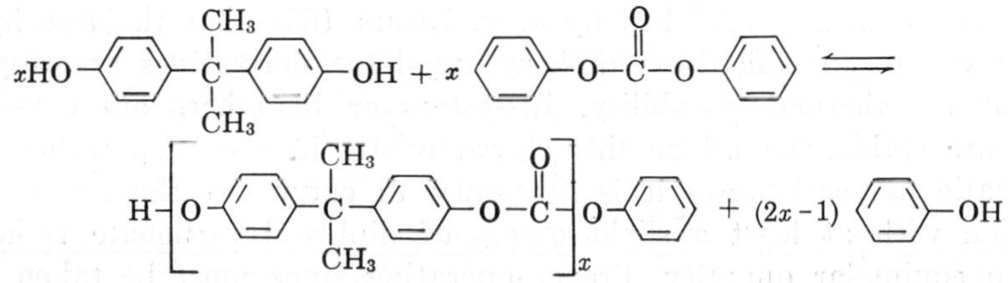

The polycondensation is an equilibrium reaction. To obtain high yields and a high molecular weight, almost complete removal of the aromatic monohydroxy compound from the reaction mixture is required.

To carry out the transesterification, temperatures between 150 and 300°C and vacuum, and at the end medium-high vacuum, are required. When using a strongly alkaline catalyst in the transesterification of 4,4'-dihydroxy-diphenyl alkanes with diphenyl carbonates, the elimination of phenol starts at about 150°C. Within 30 to 60 minutes at temperatures up to 200°C the majority of the phenol is split off, if it is removed rapidly from the reaction mixture, e.g., by the application of agitation and vacuum. After an additional 5 to 6 hours of heating with increasing temperatures up to 280–300°C and increasing vacuum the removal of phenol is complete.

The polycarbonate prepared from 4,4'-dihydroxy-diphenyl alkanes by this process is discolored and insoluble, if large quantities of catalyst are used, even if care is taken to exclude atmospheric oxygen during the polycondensation. The reason for this lies in the thermal instability of the 4,4′-dihydroxy-diphenyl alkanes and a side reaction of the Kolbe-Schmitt type; 4,4′-dihydroxy-diphenyl alkanes split into isopropenyl phenols and phenol in the presence of alkali at temperatures exceeding 150°C (section IV, 1).

(III-32)

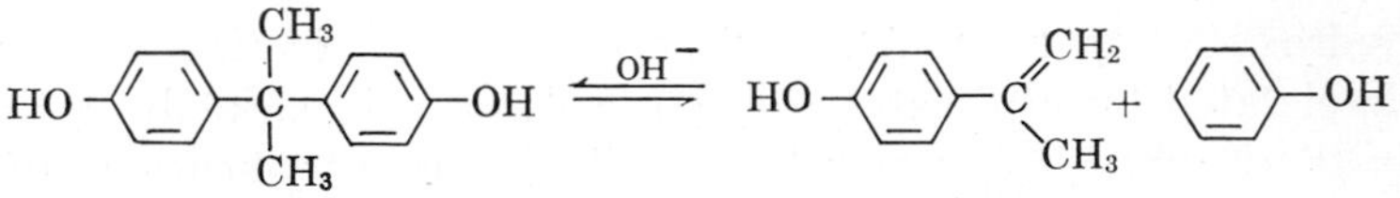

If these highly reactive, unsaturated phenols are formed during the transesterification, they will undergo polymerization and addition reactions before they can be removed from the reaction mixture by distillation.

The polymerization and addition reactions of these phenols result in undesirable colored products.

It has been established by J. v. Braun (55) that the free hydroxyl groups of the dihydroxy-diphenyl methane derivatives are responsible for the thermal instability. Bis-esters or bis-ethers are considerably more stable. To utilize this characteristic in the preparation of aromatic polycarbonates it is necessary to carry out the transesterification with at least a slight excess of diphenyl carbonate rather than an equimolar quantity. Proper operating steps must be taken to prevent the removal of diphenyl carbonate during the distillation of the by-product phenol.

Under optimum conditions it is possible to prepare, rather rapidly,

(III-33)

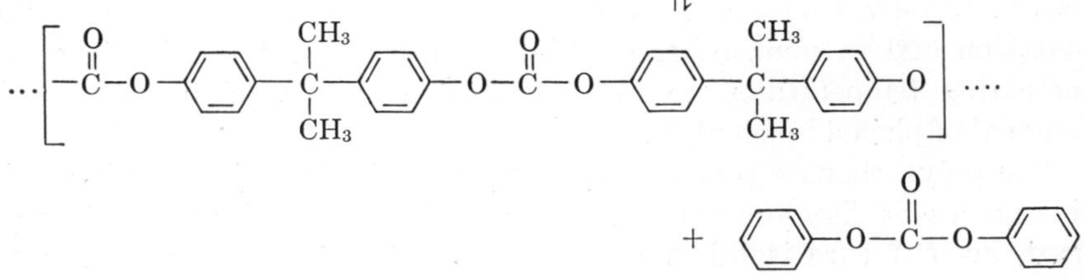

at temperatures between 150 and 200°C, low molecular weight polycarbonates terminated with phenyl carbonate end groups. At higher
temperatures and greatly reduced pressures these low molecular weight
polymers convert to high molecular weight polycarbonates with the
elimination of diphenylcarbonate. This part of the transesterification
takes place at suitable rates only at temperatures over 250°C and is
not accelerated as much by catalyst as the transesterification, which
splits out aromatic hydroxy compounds.

When the polycondensation is carried out with excess diphenyl carbonate, the presence in the transesterification reaction mixture at high
temperatures of 4,4'-dihydroxy-diphenyl alkanes with free hydroxyl
groups is so repressed that the decomposition of the bisphenols is almost nonexistent. It is also possible, however, to prepare high molecular
weight aromatic polycarbonates by transesterification with less than
the equivalent quantity of diphenyl carbonate. In this case the high
molecular state is achieved by the aromatic dihydroxy compounds
being split off (56).

Branching and crosslinking of the polycarbonate can be brought
about during the transesterification by a side reaction analogous to
the Kolbe-Schmitt reaction (27).

At high temperatures in the presence of alkaline catalysts carbonic
acid ester groups can rearrange to form an ether linkage in the polymer
backbone and a pendant free carboxyl group. These carboxyl groups
can lead to branching and crosslinking through esterification.

That this reaction is not unlikely is demonstrated by the formation
of o-phenoxybenzoic acid and its phenyl ester, besides other products,
through the action of sodium carbonate on diphenyl carbonate at temperatures above 200°C (57):

(III-35)

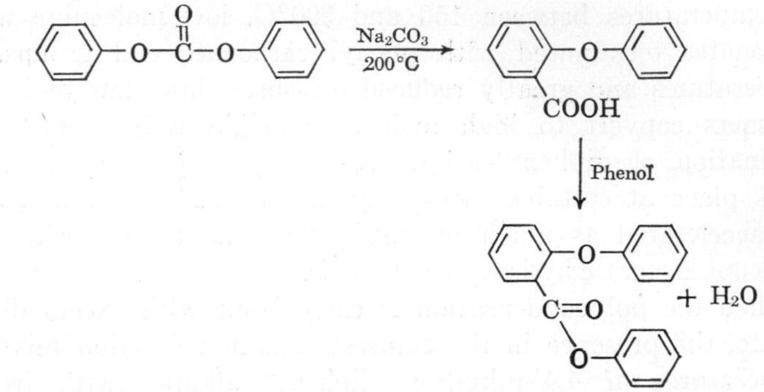

Even this side reaction, however, can be nearly elminated by the choice of the proper catalyst, used in small quantities, and by the use of raw materials of high purity.

Acids, such as boric acid, p-toluene sulfonic acid, and zinc chloride are not very effective catalysts for transesterification. Mixtures of the acetates of calcium, magnesium, zinc, tin, lead, manganese, cadmium, and cobalt with antimony compounds, such as antimony trioxide, are relatively ineffective (58).

Soluble manganese compounds are only slightly effective and result in discolored polycarbonate when used in larger quantities (59).

Basic catalysts, such as alkali metals and alkaline earth metals and their oxides, hydrides, or amides, or basic metaloxides, such as zinc oxide, lead oxide, and antimony oxide, accelerate the transesterification to a significantly greater degree (27,28).

Many catalysts for the transesterification of dicarbonylic acid esters and dihydroxy compounds, such as organotitanium and organoaluminum compounds, also lead to coloration and decomposition in the transesterification of 4,4′-dihydroxy-diphenyl alkanes with diaryl carbonates (60).

The catalysts are added at levels of 0.0001 to 0.1%, calculated on the polycarbonate formed.

The preparation of polycarbonate from bisphenol A can be carried out as follows (61):

A mixture of 456 g of 4,4′-dihydroxy-diphenyl-2,2-propane, 460 g of diphenyl carbonate, and 0.008 g of lithium hydride is melted under nitrogen at 110–150°C in a round bottom reactor equipped with a stirrer and a downflow condenser. The phenol eliminated is removed by distillation at 20 mm Hg and temperatures up to 210°C. At this point the pressure is reduced to 0.2 mm Hg, and the temperature is raised over a period of 1 hour to 250°C and to 280°C during the next 2 hours. Near the end of the polycondensation the catalyst is neutralized by the addition of 0.05 g of dimethyl sulfate, and the excess neutralizing agent is distilled out. The product is a nearly colorless, highly viscous melt which solidifies to a clear, transparent, viscoelastic plastic. The relative viscosity of the polyester, determined in a 0.5% solution in methylene chloride at 20°, is $\eta_{rel} = 1.32$.

The melt viscosity of aromatic polycarbonates is so high at temperatures up to 300° C that polyesters with molecular weights exceeding 50,000 cannot be produced in reactors and agitation systems customarily used in plastic processing; above this molecular weight the melts have rubber-elastic properties.

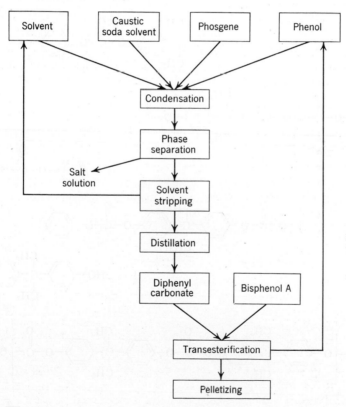

Fig. III-3. Process for the preparation of polycarbonate from bisphenol A by transesterification.

A simplified flow diagram for the transesterification process based on 4,4'-dihydroxy-diphenyl-2,2-propane is shown in Figure III-3 (62).

As a first step diphenyl carbonate is prepared by reacting phosgene with an aqueous alkaline solution of phenol in the presence of an inert solvent in a process analogous to the interfacial polycondensation of bisphenol A and phosgene (section III, 3, A, 2). After separation of the aqueous salt solution, the solvent is stripped off and the diphenyl carbonate is distilled. This is then reacted with bisphenol A. The polycarbonate is drawn from the reaction vessel in the form of rods or bands which are chopped into pellets. Solvent and phenol are returned to the process.

The special advantage of the transesterification process lies in the ease with which the chlorine can be removed as sodium chloride during the

(III–36)

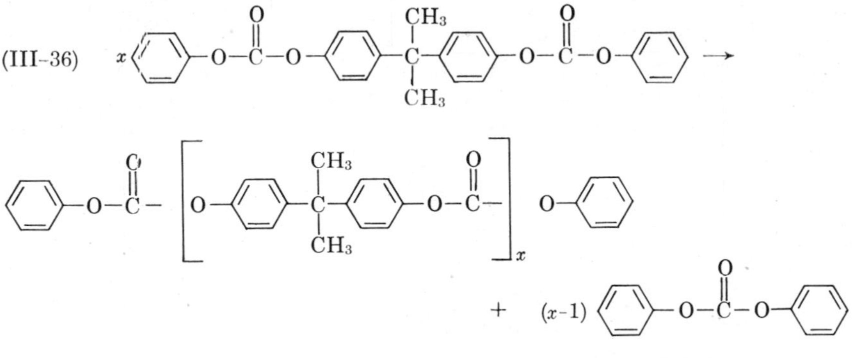

(III–37)

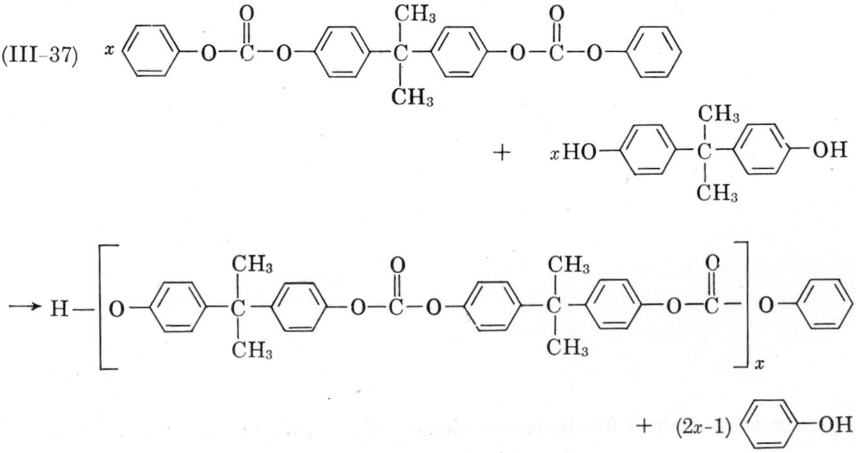

preparation of diphenyl carbonate. The diphenyl carbonate can then easily be obtained ash-free by distillation.

Another advantage is that the polycarbonate is obtained in a dry form suitable for direct pelletizing and packaging.

The disadvantages of this process lie in the mechanical difficulties associated with carrying out the polycondensation at high temperatures and at low pressures and also the limitation on the maximum molecular weight obtainable due to the high-melt viscosity.

Transesterification can also be used in the preparation of high molecular weight polycarbonates from the reaction of bis-aryl carbonates of aromatic dihydroxy compounds with themselves or with other aromatic dihydroxy compounds (27,63) (see formulas III-36 and III-37).

The transesterification of such carbonates with splitting off of diphenyl carbonate has the advantage that free aromatic dihydroxy compounds are not at any time present in the reaction mixture, which eliminates side reactions and guarantees the equivalence of the reactants throughout the whole reaction period. The disadvantage is the difficulty of removing the last trace of the high boiling diphenyl carbonate from the polyester.

The transesterification of the bisaryl carbonates of aromatic dihydroxy compounds with aromatic dihydroxy compounds had the advantage of better volume-time yield than transesterification with diphenyl carbonate, since, by way of comparison, only half as much phenol must be eliminated.

The same catalysts can be used for this reaction as are applicable to transesterification with diphenyl carbonate.

5. Other Methods of Preparation of Aromatic Polycarbonates

Three processes for the preparation of polycarbonates have been described in the preceding sections: phosgenation in the presence of pyridine (section III, 3, A, 1), interfacial polycondensation (section III, 3, A, 2), and transesterification (section III, 3, A, 4). To date no other process is of commercial significance, but considerable additional preparative methods have been reported.

Staab found that certain diamides of carbonic acid, such as N,N'-carbonyl diimidazole and N,N'-carbonyl ditriazole are able to react with aliphatic and aromatic hydroxy and amino compounds with introduction of carbonyl groups (64).

N,N'-Carbonyl diimidazole can be prepared in good yields by the reaction of 4 moles of imidazole and 1 mole of phosgene. The reaction must be carried out in the absence of water, since N,N'-carbonyl diimid-

(III-38)

$$4 \begin{array}{c} N=CH \\ | \quad \diagdown \\ \quad \quad NH \\ | \quad \diagup \\ HC=CH \end{array} + COCl_2 \rightarrow \begin{array}{c} N=CH \quad \quad O \quad \quad CH=N \\ | \quad \diagdown \quad \| \quad \diagup \quad | \\ \quad \quad N-C-N \\ | \quad \diagup \quad \quad \quad \diagdown \quad | \\ HC=CH \quad \quad \quad \quad CH=CH \end{array} + 2 \, Imid \cdot HCl$$

azole (melting point 90°C, boiling point 256°C) is rapidly hydrolyzed by water even during storage in moist air. The decomposition products are CO_2 and imidazole. The reaction of this compound with aromatic dihydroxy compounds in the absence of water and in inert solvents, such as tetrahydrofuran and methylene chloride, yields aromatic polycarbonates (65).

(III-39)

$$x HO-\bigcirc-\underset{\underset{CH_3}{|}}{\overset{\overset{CH_3}{|}}{C}}-\bigcirc-OH + x \begin{array}{c} N=CH \quad O \quad CH=N \\ \diagdown \quad \| \quad \diagup \\ N-C-N \\ \diagup \quad \quad \diagdown \\ CH=CH \quad CH=CH \end{array} \rightarrow$$

$$H-\left[-O-\bigcirc-\underset{\underset{CH_3}{|}}{\overset{\overset{CH_3}{|}}{C}}-\bigcirc-O-\overset{\overset{O}{\|}}{C}-\right]_x -N\begin{array}{c} \diagup CH=N \\ | \\ \diagdown CH=CH \end{array} + (2x-1) \begin{array}{c} N=CH \\ | \quad \diagdown \\ \quad \quad NH \\ | \quad \diagup \\ CH=CH \end{array}$$

The imidazole so formed must be removed completely from the solution of polycarbonate, for example, by extraction of the solution with dilute hydrochloric acid and water, since even a small quantity of the base results in discoloration and decomposition reactions during the thermoplastic processing of the polycarbonate. Further disadvantages are (a) for an economical process it is necessary to effect complete recovery of the imidazole from both steps (4 moles); (b) N,N'-carbonyl diimidazole is sensitive to water. For these reasons either phosgenation in the presence of pyridine or the interfacial polycondensation is to be preferred to the foregoing process.

The reaction of 4,4'-dihydroxy-diphenyl alkanes with N,N'-carbonyl diimidazole in melts leads to colored low-molecular polycarbonates due to promotion of decomposition of bisphenols and polycarbonates by imidazole (65).

Diesters of aromatic dihydroxy compounds may be transesterified with diaryl carbonates, in which case polycarbonate is formed by the splitting out of the phenol ester. From the diacetate of the bisphenol A, for example, in transesterification with diphenyl carbonate, a polycarbonate is formed as phenyl acetate is split out (66).

By heating the polycarbonate copolymer prepared from ethylene glycol bis-chlorocarbonic acid and bisphenol A to 280°C in medium high-

(III-40) $\cdots$ $\left[O-\!\!\!\!\bigcirc\!\!\!\!-\overset{\overset{\displaystyle CH_3}{|}}{\underset{\underset{\displaystyle CH_3}{|}}{C}}-\!\!\!\!\bigcirc\!\!\!\!-O-\overset{\overset{\displaystyle O}{\|}}{C}-O-CH_2-CH_2-O-\overset{\overset{\displaystyle O}{\|}}{C}- \right]_x$ $\cdots$

$\rightarrow \cdots$ $\left[O-\!\!\!\!\bigcirc\!\!\!\!-\overset{\overset{\displaystyle CH_3}{|}}{\underset{\underset{\displaystyle CH_3}{|}}{C}}-\!\!\!\!\bigcirc\!\!\!\!-O-\overset{\overset{\displaystyle O}{\|}}{C}- \right]_x$ $\cdots + x \begin{array}{c} CH_2-O \\ | \quad\quad\;\; \diagdown \\ \quad\quad\quad C=O \\ | \quad\quad\;\; \diagup \\ CH_2-O \end{array}$

vacuum, Sweeny obtained the polycarbonate from bisphenol A (67). The tendency for the formation of the cyclic 5-membered ethylene glycol carbonate (section III, 1, A) under these conditions is very great. As a result, the aromatic polycarbonate can be formed from the aromatic-aliphatic polycarbonate copolymer with elimination of the volatile glycol carbonate.

Schnell and Bottenbruch (68) prepared cyclic tetrameric carbonates by reaction of 4,4'-dihydroxy-diphenyl-2,2-propane, 4,4'-dihydroxy-di-phenyl-1,1-cyclohexane, 4,4'-dihydroxy-3,3'-dimethyl-diphenyl-2,2-propane, 4,4'-dihydroxy-3,3',5,5'-tetrachloro-diphenyl-2,2-propane, and 4,4'-dihydroxy-diphenyl-sulfide with the bis-chlorocarbonic esters of the same dihydroxy compounds in pyridine using the Ziegler-Ruggli dilution principle.

These cyclic carbonates polymerize at high temperatures under the action of alkaline catalysts yielding aromatic polycarbonates with extremely high molecular weights and narrow molecular weight distributions.

6. Preparation of Polycarbonate Copolymers and Mixed Polycondensates Containing Carbonate Groups

This section describes the preparation of polycarbonate copolymers from various aromatic or aromatic and aliphatic dihydroxy compounds and also mixed polycondensates which contain, in addition to carbonic acid ester groups, other groups such as carboxylic acid ester, urethane, urea, or siloxane groups.

A. POLYCARBONATE COPOLYMERS. A large number of starting materials can be used for the preparation of polycarbonate copolymers from various aromatic dihydroxy compounds, such as hydroquinone, resorcinol, dihydroxy-diphenyl, dihydroxy-naphthalene, dihydroxy-diphenyl alkanes. dihydroxy-diphenyl ether, dihydroxy-diphenyl sulfide, dihydroxy-diphenyl sulfoxide or sulfone, and the ring halogenated or alkylated derivatives of these compounds.

From mixtures of the above described dihydroxy compounds used in various ratios an almost indefinite number of polycarbonate copolymers can be envisioned. Polycarbonate copolymers can be prepared by phosgenation in the presence of pyridine (section III, 3, A, 1), interfacial polycondensation (section III, 3, A, 2), or transesterification (section III, 3, A, 4), when they are soluble, or by transesterification when they are meltable but not soluble in the usual solvents used for the phosgenation processes (27,28,62,69,70,71,72,73,74,75).

Randomly built up polymers are formed if the reactivity of the various aromatic dihydroxy compounds toward carbonic acid derivatives is comparable, which is often the case. The properties of the polycarbonate copolymers formed are, of course, influenced by the ratio and the type of the dihydroxy compounds used.

The transesterification of mixtures of various aromatic dihydroxy compounds with diaryl carbonates, such as diphenyl carbonate, does not give rise to any difficulties, provided that the polycarbonate copolymers melt below their decomposition temperature (70,76).

Because of their increased acidity, halogen-substituted aromatic dihydroxy compounds esterify more rapidly with bis-carbonates of halogenated aromatic hydroxy compounds than with diphenyl carbonate. It is therefore advantageous to react mixtures of various halogenated dihydroxy compounds, as well as mixtures of aromatic dihydroxy compounds with halogenated aromatic dihydroxy compounds, with bis-carbonates of halogenated aromatic hydroxy compounds such as bis-(2,6-dichlorophenyl) carbonate (77).

By a special process it is possible to prepare polycarbonate block copolymers from various aromatic dihydroxy compounds. For this purpose solutions of low molecular weight polycarbonates with —OCOCl end groups are prepared in separate reactors from several aromatic dihydroxy compounds by employing the interfacial polycondensation method. These solutions are then mixed and by the addition of amine catalysts, such as tri-n-butylamine, converted into solutions of high molecular weight polycarbonate block copolymers.

The composition, the length of the sections, and the molecular weight of the block copolymers can be varied by controlling the molecular weight of the polycarbonates and the mixing ratio. The polycarbonate can be recovered from the solution by the usual methods (section III, 3, A, 3). Compared with mixtures of the individual polycarbonates, the block copolymers have a higher melting range and a higher modulus of elasticity (78). Compared to the respective homopolycondensates, they have a higher flexibility and a higher modulus of elasticity (Chapter V).

The polycarbonate block copolymers described in Table III-5 have been prepared by this process.

The preparation of polycarbonate copolymers from aromatic and aliphatic dihydroxy compounds gives rise to greater difficulties due to

TABLE III-5

Polycarbonate Block Copolymers from Various Aromatic
Dihydroxy-Compounds

Polycarbonate block copolymer from		Reference
4,4′-Dihydroxy-diphenyl-2,2-propane	3,3′,5,5′-tetrachloro-4,4′-dihydroxy-diphenyl-2,2-propane	(79)
"	4,4′-dihydroxy-tetraphenyl methane	(80)
"	4,4′-dihydroxy-triphenyl methyl methane	(81)
"	4,4′-dihydroxy-diphenyl-methyl-4-chlorophenyl methane	(81)
"	4,4′-dihydroxy-diphenyl-methyl-3,4-dichlorophenyl methane	(81)
"	4,4′-dihydroxy-diphenyl-methyl-2,5-dichlorophenyl methane	(81)
"	4,4′-dihydroxy-diphenyl-2-chloro-phenyl methane	(82)
"	4,4′-dihydroxy-diphenyl-methyl-4-fluorophenyl methane	(82)
"	4,4′-dihydroxy-diphenyl-naphthyl methane	(83)
"	4,4′-dihydroxy-diphenyl-2-(1-chloronaphthyl)methane	(83)
3,3′,5,5′-Tetrachloro-4,4′-dihydroxy-diphenyl-2,2-propane	4,4′-dihydroxy-diphenyl-naphthyl methane	(84)
"	4,4′-dihydroxy-diphenyl-2(1-chloronaphthyl)methane	(84)
4,4′-Dihydroxy-triphenyl methyl methane	4,4′-dihydroxy-diphenyl-methyl-3,4-dichlorophenyl methane	(85)
"	4,4′-dihydroxy-diphenyl-methyl-2,5-dichlorophenyl methane	(85)

(a) differences in the reactivity of the aromatic and aliphatic hydroxyl group with carbonic acid derivates, (b) the water solubility of some aliphatic dihydroxy compounds, and (c) the comparatively limited thermal stability of the aliphatic carbonates. For those cases in which polycarbonate copolymers soluble in an inert solvent are to be made, the phosgenation of mixtures of aliphatic and aromatic dihydroxy compounds in mixtures of pyridine and inert solvents, such as methylene chloride, is attractive, since the reactivity of the aromatic and aliphatic hydroxyl groups with the pyridine, phosgene and pyridine, and chlorocarbonate adducts is not very different (section III, 3, A, *1*). In this way a large number of polycarbonate copolymers were prepared from aromatic dihydroxy compounds, such as hydroquinone, 4,4′-dihydroxy-diphenyl, 4,4′-dihydroxy-diphenyl alkanes, 4,4′-dihydroxy-diphenyl ethers, 4,4′dihydroxy-diphenyl sulfides, 4,4′-dihydroxy-diphenyl sulfoxides, and 4,4′-dihydroxy-diphenyl sulfones, with aliphatic dihydroxy compounds, such as ethylene glycol, 1,4-butanediol, 1,6-hexanediol, 4,4′-dihydroxy-dicyclohexyl-2,2-propane, etc. (70,76,86). The amine-catalyzed interfacial polycondensation of mixtures of aliphatic and aromatic dihydroxy compounds (section III, 3, A, *2*) by phosgenation of an aqueous alkaline phase and a water insoluble inert solvent phase results in the complete building in of the aliphatic dihydroxy compound only if it is nearly or completely water-insoluble. Water-soluble aliphatic dihydroxy compounds, such as ethylene glycol, are not built in or are built in only in part into the macromolecule by this process. Polycarbonate copolymers based on 4,4′-dihydroxy-diphenyl-2,2-propane and 1,6-hexanediol have been prepared by the interfacial polycondensation process as an example (70). Phosgenation in the presence of pyridine as well as in the interfacial polycondensation method cannot lead to a completely random copolymer because of the difference in the reactivities of the aromatic and aliphatic dihydroxy compounds toward phosgene. Experiments to confirm this have not been made to date. In 1943 W. Kimpel produced aliphatic-aromatic copolycarbonates of relatively low molecular weight by reaction of the bis-chlorocarbonic acid esters of aliphatic dihydroxy compounds with aromatic dihydroxy compounds in an aqueous alkaline medium (87). High molecular weight, high melting aliphatic-aromatic copolycarbonates were later produced by reaction of bis-chlorocarbonic acid esters of aliphatic dihydroxy compounds with aromatic dihydroxy compounds, or of bis-chlorocarbonic acid esters of aromatic dihydroxy compounds with aliphatic dihydroxy compounds in a mixture of pyridine and an inert solvent, or by using the amine-catalyzed interfacial polycondensation in a two-phase mixture of aqueous alkali hydroxide and a water insoluble inert solvent (67, 70,76). Using these techniques copolycarbonates with a relatively regular buildup of the molecular chain can be produced.

The preparation of the bis-chlorocarbonic acid esters of aliphatic dihydroxy compounds in a purity sufficient for the preparation of high molecular weight polycarbonate copolymers is difficult. It was therefore proposed that by the interfacial polycondensation method aromatic dihydroxy compounds be reacted with a slight excess of the bis-chlorocarbonic acid ester of an aliphatic dihydroxy compound to obtain a solution of a low molecular weight polycarbonate copolymer with —OCOCl end groups. The —OCOCl end groups could then be hydrolyzed and the high molecular weight state finally achieved by phosgenation (88).

Aromatic-aliphatic polycarbonate block copolymers can be prepared by reacting the bis-chlorocarbonic acid esters of polymeric compounds with terminal aliphatic hydroxyl groups, such as polyethylene glycol, polytetrahydrofuran glycol, polyethylene adipate, or polystyrene, with low molecular weight aromatic polycarbonates with OH end groups by the process of interfacial polycondensation (89).

The reaction of bis-chlorocarbonic acid esters of aromatic dihydroxy compounds, which can be prepared readily in high purity, with aliphatic dihydroxy compounds (70,85) in mixtures of pyridine and inert solvents does not give any special trouble. By the interfacial condensation method, again the water-soluble aliphatic dihydroxy compounds do not or will only partially build into a macromolecule.

The preparation of polycarbonate copolymers from aromatic and aliphatic dihydroxy compounds by the transesterification process will take place only at a sufficient velocity if diaryl carbonates, such as diphenyl carbonate, are utilized as the transesterification compound.

The thermal stability of these polycarbonates copolymers is even lower than that of aliphatic polycarbonates. This reduced thermal stability, when compared to that of aromatic polycarbonates, must be taken into account during the transesterification by the utilization of very small amounts of alkaline transesterification catalysts and by the use of mild transesterification conditions.

This is possible in many cases because the melting point of the polycarbonate copolymers from aromatic and aliphatic dihydroxy compounds is lower than that of the pure aromatic polycarbonates and polycarbonate copolymers. In transesterification temperatures of 200°C and a maximum of 250°C should not be exceeded (70). At higher temperatures the polycarbonate copolymer from 4,4'-dihydroxy-diphenyl propane and ethylene glycol (prepared from ethylene glycol bis-chlorocarbonic acid ester and bisphenol A) splits out the cyclic 5-membered glycol carbonate and changes into the aromatic polycarbonate (67). Polycarbonate copolymers from aromatic dihydroxy compounds with other aliphatic dihydroxy compounds decompose at higher temperatures by degradation of the macromolecule and the formation of undefined decomposition products. Bisaryl carbonates of aromatic dihydroxy compounds can also be transesterified with aliphatic dihydroxy compound to polycarbonate copolymers (76).

By mixed polycondensation of bisalkyl carbonates of aromatic-aliphatic hydroxy compounds, such as 1,4-bis-(β-hydroxyethyl)benzene bis-ethyl carbonate, 4,4'-bis-(β-hydroxyethyl)diphenyl bisethyl carbonate, or bisalkyl carbonates of oxyethylated aromatic dihydroxy compounds with one another or with bisalkyl carbonates of aliphatic dihydroxy compounds in accordance with the process described in section III, 2, with heavy metal catalysts, a large number of polycarbonate copolymers have become accessible which are said to be particularly suitable for the production of films and fibers (90).

B. MIXED POLYESTERS CONTAINING CARBONIC ACID ESTER GROUPS AS WELL AS CARBOXYLIC ACID ESTER GROUPS. Mixed polyesters which contain carboxyl acid ester groups in addition to carbonic acid ester groups can be prepared by the substitution of a part of the phosgene by aliphatic or aromatic dicarboxylic acid chlorides. Such preparations can be made in the usual way in process mixtures of pyridine and inert solvents (91) or by interfacial condensation (92).

In the first-mentioned process it is possible to use the dicarboxylic acids (91) instead of the acid chlorides, since the dicarboxylic acids are first converted to the acid chlorides with the phosgene in the presence of pyridine. If the aromatic dihydroxy compound is first reacted with phosgene in less than equimolar quantities and finally with dicarboxylic acid and phosgene, block copolymers are obtained. These can also be produced if solutions of low molecular weight polyesters are prepared from aromatic dihydroxy compounds, dicarboxylic acids, and phosgene and then mixed with a solution of low molecular weight aromatic polycarbonates and phosgenated in the presence of pyridine to reach a high molecular weight (91).

Similarly, mixed polyesters containing carbonate groups result from the reaction of low molecular weight polyesters with hydroxyl end groups with phosgene in the presence of pyridine and an inert solvent. Polyesters from phthalic acid and ethylene or propylene glycol may be used (93). Diesters of aromatic hydroxycarboxylic acids with aliphatic dihydroxy compounds, e.g., the di-p-hydroxybenzoate of ethylene glycol or ethylene glycol divanillate, may also be used as starting materials for the phosgenation in mixture of pyridine and inert solvents or in the interfacial polycondensation method (94).

The transesterification process can also be utilized for the preparation of polycarbonate block copolymers containing carboxylic acid ester groups. In this case in the transesterification of aromatic dihydroxy compounds with diaryl carbonates a part of the diaryl carbonate is substituted by diaryl esters of aliphatic or aromatic dicarboxylic acids, and the transesterification is carried out as usual.

Aliphatic and aromatic carboxylic acids or dicarboxylic acids give the corresponding aryl esters when heated with diaryl carbonates in the

$$\text{(III-41)} \quad \underset{\substack{\| \\ O}}{R-C-OH} + \text{C}_6\text{H}_5-O-\underset{\substack{\| \\ O}}{C}-O-\text{C}_6\text{H}_5 \longrightarrow$$

$$\underset{\substack{\| \\ O}}{R-C}-O-\text{C}_6\text{H}_5 + CO_2 + \text{C}_6\text{H}_5-OH$$

presence of alkaline catalysts (95). Consequently, the free acids can be used instead of the aryl esters (96). It is best to carry out the reaction in a manner that the mixture of aromatic dihydroxy compounds, dicarboxylic acid, and diphenyl carbonate is agitated at temperatures of 200°C until the carbon dioxide evolution has ended. The esterification is continued with removal of phenol under medium-high and high vacuum, as described in section III, 3, A, 4, until the desired molecular weight is reached. The quantity of the diphenyl carbonate added must be so regulated that two moles are available for each mole of the dicarboxylic acid and one mole for each mole of aromatic dihydroxy compound still present in the reaction mixture after esterification with the dicarboxylic acid diyphenyl ester. A larger excess of diphenyl carbonate should be avoided, since it decreases the reaction velocity.

Low molecular weight polyesters may be substituted for a part of the aromatic dihydroxy compound during the esterification with diphenyl carbonate. These polyesters build into the macromolecule during the transesterification through their free hydroxyl or carboxyl end groups. Transesterification of mixtures of 4,4'-dihydroxy-diphenyl-2,2-propane and low molecular weight polyesters made from terephthalic acid and ethylene glycol with diphenyl carbonate leads to soluble copolymers which are said to show easier workability in thermoplastic processing than does polycarbonate from bisphenol A (97).

The carbonate groups can also be built into the polyester by transesterification of the dialkyl esters of aromatic dicarboxylic acids, e.g., dimethyl terephthalate, with mixtures of aliphatic dihydroxy compounds, such as ethylene glycol, and bis-(ω-hydroxyalkyl) carbonates, such as bis-(β-hydroxyethyl) carbonate. In these processes, however, special organometallic transesterification catalysts must be used (section III, 1, A, 3 and 4) to avoid the thermal splitting of the aliphatically bound carbonate groups (98). The soluble copolymers which result have melt temperatures lower than the comparable polyester.

C. MIXED POLYESTERS CONTAINING CARBONIC ACID ESTER GROUPS AS WELL AS URETHANE GROUPS. Carbamic acid esters (urethanes) are formed in a smooth reaction from aliphatic and aromatic chlorocarbonic acid esters and amines at low temperatures in the presence of an acid-accepting reagent. Many attempts have therefore been made to prepare polyester urethanes by reacting bis-chlorocarbonic acid esters of aliphatic or aromatic dihydroxy compounds with mixtures of dihydroxy compounds and diamines (99) or by the reaction of low molecular weight aromatic polycarbonate with —OCOCl end groups with diamines (100).

If a high molecular weight polycarbonate from bisphenol A is reacted in solution with aliphatic primary or secondary diamines, degradation takes place which leads to copolycarbonate urethanes with phenolic end groups and in the final state to urethane bisphenol.

These urethane bisphenols can be converted with phosgene in pyridine or by the interfacial polycondensation method into high molecular weight copolycarbonate urethanes which are said to be more resistant to hydrolysis than the polycarbonate made from bisphenol A (101). A disadvantage of these products is the low thermal stability of the urethane group. The aryl esters of carbamic acid split at temperatures above 150°C into isocyanates and aromatic hydroxy compounds. The alkyl esters of carbamic acid decompose above 200°C.

D. MIXED POLYESTERS CONTAINING CARBONIC ACID ESTER GROUPS AS WELL AS IMINE CARBONATE OR SILOXANE GROUPS. When part of the phosgene is substituted with cyanogen chloride in the amine-catalyzed interfacial polycondensation of aromatic dihydroxy compounds, mixed polymers result in which a part of the carbonate groups is replaced by the

$$-O-\overset{\|}{\underset{NH}{C}}-O-\text{group (102)}.$$ The melting ranges of these mixed polymers is lower than that of the corresponding aromatic polycarbonates.

Silicon-containing polycarbonate copolymers can be obtained by the substitution of part of the phosgene with organodihalogen silanes, such as dimethyl dichlorosilane, in the reaction of aromatic dihydroxy compounds in mixtures of pyridine and inert solvents. In these polysiloxane

$$\text{carbonates part of the carbonate groups is replaced by the } -O-\overset{R}{\underset{R}{\overset{|}{Si}}}-O-$$

group. These polymers melt substantially lower than the comparable aromatic polycarbonates (103).

Of greater practical importance to date are the copolymers from 4,4′-dihydroxy-diphenyl-2,2-propane and small quantities of other aromatic dihydroxy compounds or aromatic dicarboxylic acids, which should show reduced crystallization tendency when compared to polycarbonate made from 4,4′-dihydroxy-diphenyl-2,2-propane alone.

7. Crosslinking of Polycarbonates

The commercially used aromatic polycarbonates are high melting thermoplastics soluble in common solvents. In some applications it is an advantage to reduce the solubility and the swelling in organic solvents and to raise the heat distortion point. Both results can be achieved by primary crosslinking of the linear macromolecules. Such crosslinking can be obtained in polycarbonate to a limited degree by the effect of ionizing radiation, by the effect of chemical materials, such as oxygen, formaldehyde, substances which form formaldehyde (104), or poly-epoxides at higher temperature, as well as by heating those polycarbonates which have groups on the macromolecule with tendencies to cross-linking reactions.

Since crosslinking results in an insoluble and unmeltable product, which can only be machined for further work, the crosslinking reaction must be performed during or after the preparation of the molded article.

A. INFLUENCE OF RADIATION ON AROMATIC POLYCARBONATES AND POLYCARBONATE COPOLYMERS. Under the influence of ionizing radiation, such as high-energy electrons, neutrons, X-rays, or gamma rays on macromolecular substances, crosslinking or degradation of the macromolecule may take place. It is highly probable that in the irradiation hydrogen atoms are first split out with the formation of free radicals. These macroradicals may lead to primary crosslinking or to chain breaking and the formation of carbon to carbon double bonds (105).

Compared to many other plastics, the aromatic polycarbonates based on 4,4'-dihydroxy-diphenyl alkanes are very resistant to ionizing radiation (106). Specific radiation dosages between approximately 20 and 50 $\times$ 10^6 rep even improve the physical properties of polycarbonate based on 4,4'-dihydroxy-diphenyl-2,2-propane. The tensile strength of films or sheets from this polycarbonate, irradiated in air with electrons, is increased and the softening temperature is raised. The notched impact strength of injection-molded articles is increased (Chapter V). If the optimum doses are exceeded, the values decrease again (107). The behavior of this polycarbonate is similar when it is irradiated with gamma rays from a cobalt-60 source in air or under vacuum (106). Because of the irradiation the test pieces did not become insoluble and the solution viscosity decreased.

The aromatic polycarbonate turns green during the irradiation, and the coloration slowly disappears after the irradiation is finished as the oxygen diffuses throughout the polymer. The speed of the destruction of the free radicals in an X-ray irradiated polycarbonate from 4,4'-dihydroxy-diphenyl-2,2-propane was followed through optic and paramagnetic electron resonance measurements (108).

The experiments completed to date indicate that the free radicals formed during the irradiation of aromatic polycarbonate with ionizing radiation stabilize themselves by crosslinking, by degradation, by chain breaking, or by reaction with the oxygen in the air.

In dosages between approximately 20 and 50 $\times$ 10^6 rep branching and crosslinking lead to improved physical properties but are lost again following higher dosages due to chain breaking taking place simultaneously.

The aromatic polycarbonates are very stable against visible and ultraviolet light, even in the presence of air (Chapter V).

In the mixed polycondensation of 4,4'-dihydroxy-diaryl compounds, which contain in the molecule (109) a group with other aromatic di-

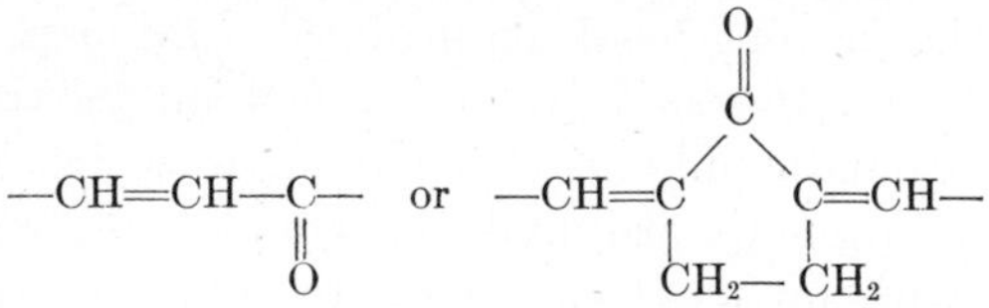

$$
—CH{=}CH—\underset{\underset{O}{\|}}{C}— \quad \text{or} \quad —CH{=}\underset{\underset{CH_2—CH_2}{|}}{C}\overset{\overset{O}{\|}}{\diagdown}\overset{C}{\diagdown}C{=}CH—
$$

hydroxy compounds, a polycarbonate copolymer is obtained, which can be crosslinked by the action of short-wavelength visual light or ultraviolet light. Suitable aromatic dihydroxy compounds are, as an example, 1,4-phenylene bis-(4-hydroxyphenyl vinyl ketone), which can be prepared from terephthaldialdehyde and 4-hydroxyacetophenone (110) or

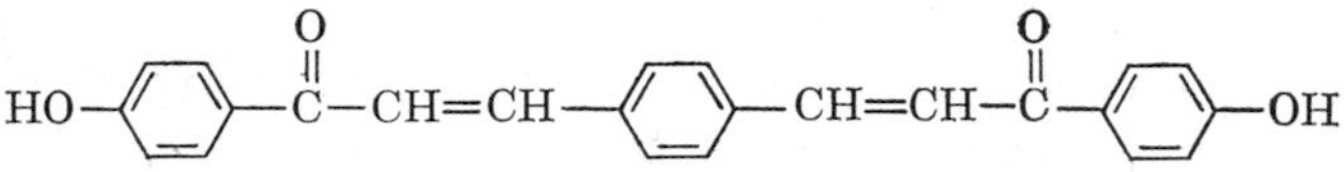

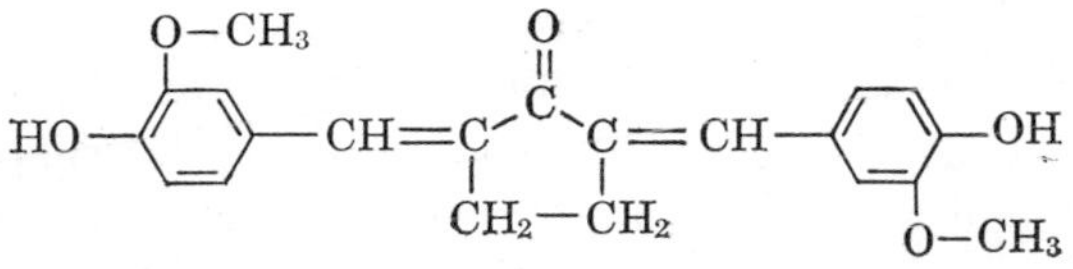

$$
HO{-}\langle\bigcirc\rangle{-}\overset{\overset{O}{\|}}{C}{-}CH{=}CH{-}\langle\bigcirc\rangle{-}CH{=}CH{-}\overset{\overset{O}{\|}}{C}{-}\langle\bigcirc\rangle{-}OH
$$

$$
HO{-}\overset{\overset{O-CH_3}{|}}{\langle\bigcirc\rangle}{-}CH{=}\underset{\underset{CH_2-CH_2}{|}}{C}\overset{\overset{O}{\|}}{\diagup}\overset{C}{\diagdown}C{=}CH{-}\underset{\underset{O-CH_3}{|}}{\langle\bigcirc\rangle}{-}OH
$$

divanyllal cyclopentanone (109). For mixed condensation of these compounds with other aromatic dihydroxy compounds, the amine-catalyzed interfacial polycondensation as well as the transesterification process can be used advantageously. Instead of the unsaturated aromatic dihydroxy compounds, their bis-hydroxyalkyl ethers can also be utilized (110). Formed structures, such as films or fibers, made from these polycarbonate copolymers become insoluble through crosslinking by irradiation with visible or ultraviolet light. It has therefore been proposed to utilize such films in the graphic-arts field (109,110).

B. CROSSLINKING OF AROMATIC POLYCARBONATES BY HEATING IN THE PRESENCE OF AIR. Aromatic polycarbonates are stable over long time periods at temperatures up to 150°C, also in the presence of air (Chapter V). If films from polycarbonate based on 4,4'-dihydroxy-diphenyl alkanes are kept in the presence of oxygen for long periods at temperatures around 250°C, or for short time periods at temperatures around 400°C, crosslinking takes place. The polycarbonate becomes insoluble and unmeltable. This thermal oxidative crosslinking can be utilized, for example, in the wire-coating field (111).

C. CROSSLINKING OF POLYCARBONATES AND POLYCARBONATE COPOLYMERS CONTAINING TRI- OR POLYFUNCTIONAL GROUPS. Crosslinking of liquid or low-melting polyesters containing higher than difunctional components during or after the forming has been utilized in the past in many applications (Chapter II). It was therefore logical in the transesterification of mixtures of aromatic dihydroxy compounds which contained more than difunctional aliphatic polyhydroxy compounds, e.g., glycerine or pentaerythritol, with diphenyl carbonate to stop the transesterification before the gelation took place. The soluble and meltable polycarbonate copolymers prepared in this manner were crosslinked by heating in thin layers at temperatures above 200°C. Polyalkanol amines, e.g., diethanol amine, have also been reported to be suitable for this process as polyfunctional compounds (112). The low molecular weight crosslinkable polycarbonate copolymers prepared in this manner can be used as binders in baking enamels.

Another process for the preparation of low molecular weight crosslinkable polycarbonates comprises the introduction of aliphatic compounds containing epoxy groups into the macromolecule as end groups. The glycidyl ether group can be introduced into aromatic polycarbonates or polycarbonate copolymers, and also into polycarbonate copolymers from aromatic and aliphatic dihydroxy compounds of low- or middle-range molecular weight, by the reaction of the polyester in solution or dispersion with epichlorohydrin in the presence of an acid-accepting material. Especially advantageous is the preparation of these polycarbonates or polycarbonate copolymers by the interfacial polycondensation process and to carry out the reaction with epichlorohydrin simultaneously with the phosgenation, or following the phosgenation, in the same reaction vessel. In this way polycarbonates or polycarbonate copolymers with glycidyl ether end groups result. By heating them with acid or basic hardening materials usual in the technology of the epoxy resins they transform into an insoluble and unmeltable material with excellent mechanical and electrical properties (113). The resins can be utilized as binders, molding resins, cements, or raw materials for surface coatings.

Aromatic dihydroxy compounds, which contain at least one additional functional group in the molecule suitable for a crosslinking reaction, can be utilized for the preparation of crosslinkable polycarbonates or polycarbonate copolymers. Examples of such compounds include 3,5-dihydroxy-benzoic acid ethyl ester (I), bis-(4-hydroxy-3-carboxylic acid phenyl ester) phenyl methane (II), 2,2-(4,4'-dihydroxy-diphenyl) butyric acid ethyl ester (III), or 3,3'-diallyl-4,4'-dihydroxy-diphenyl-2,2-propane (IV).

For the preparation of polycarbonates or polycarbonate copolymers with compounds of the type I to III it is advantageous to use the interfacial polycondensation process, since in this way high molecular weight products can be prepared without any danger of premature crosslinking. If these polycarbonates or polycarbonate copolymers, or their mixture with aromatic or aliphatic polyfunctional hydroxy compounds, are heated to temperatures between 250 and 300°C, crosslinking takes place; in this manner insoluble and unmeltable parts can be prepared (114). These products can be used as thermosetting resins or as baking enamels.

β-Alkenyl-substituted aromatic dihydroxy compounds, e.g., allyl hydro-

quinone or 3,3'-diallyl-4,4'-dihydroxy-diphenyl, can be prepared by a Claisen rearrangement of the corresponding allyl ether compounds of the type 3,3'-diallyl-4,4'-dihydroxy-diphenyl-2,2-propane (IV) in the same manner or by condensation of β-alkenyl-substituted aromatic hydroxy compounds with ketones or aldehydes. Polycarbonates or polycarbonate copolymers which contain these β-alkenyl-substituted aromatic dihydroxy compounds may be thermoplastic soluble polyesters, which crosslink to insoluble and unmeltable coatings when exposed to air at elevated temperatures in thin films; this crosslinking takes place especially rapidly in the presence of drying accelerators, such as cobalt naphthenate. The products obtained have good mechanical or electrical properties (115). Solution of these polycarbonates or polycarbonate copolymers in polymerizable vinyl compounds, e.g., styrene, can be changed by the use of redox catalysts at room temperature or peroxides at elevated tempera-

TABLE III-6. Aromatic Polycarbonates

Polycarbonate from	Melting range [°C]	Second-order transition temp. [°C]	Reference
1. 4,4'-Dihydroxy-diphenyl methane	223–225	147	...
2. 4,4'-Dihydroxy-3,3',5,5'-tetrachloro-diphenyl methane	234–239	...	...
3. 4,4'-Dihydroxy-diphenyl-1,1-ethane	185–195	130	(27)
4. 4,4'-Dihydroxy-diphenyl-1,1-butane	150–170	123	(27)
5. 4,4'-Dihydroxy-diphenyl-1,1-isobutane	170–180	149	(27)
6. 4,4'-Dihydroxy-diphenyl-1,1-cyclopentane	240–250	167	(27,69)
7. 4,4'-Dihydroxy-diphenyl-1,1-cyclohexane	250–260	171	(27)
8. 4,4'-Dihydroxy-3,3',5,5'-tetrachloro-diphenyl-1,1-cyclohexane	260–270	163	(69)
9. 4,4'-Dihydroxy-diphenyl phenyl methane	200–215	121	(27)
10. 4,4'-Dihydroxy-diphenyl-2-chlorophenyl methane	225	...	(82,84)
11. 4,4'-Dihydroxy-diphenyl-2,4-dichloro-phenyl methane	187	...	(82,84)
12. 4,4'-Dihydroxy-diphenyl-p-isopropyl phenyl methane	189	...	(82,84)
13. 4,4'-Dihydroxy-diphenyl naphthyl methane	215	...	(82,84)
14. 4,4'-Dihydroxy-diphenyl-2,2-propane	220–230	149	(27)
15. 4,4'-Dihydroxy-3-methyl-diphenyl-2,2-propane	210–220	140	...
16. 4,4'-Dihydroxy-3-cyclohexyl-diphenyl-2,2-propane	192–195	132	...
17. 4,4'-Dihydroxy-3-methoxy-diphenyl-2,2-propane	215–222	145	...
18. 4,4'-Dihydroxy-3-isopropyl-diphenyl-2,2-propane	200–220	112	...
19. 4,4'-Dihydroxy-3,3'-dimethyl-diphenyl-2,2-propane	150–170	95	(27,69)
20. 4,4'-Dihydroxy-3,3'-dichloro-diphenyl-2,2-propane	190–210	147	(69)
21. 4,4'-Dihydroxy-3,3',5,5'-tetrachloro-diphenyl-2,2-propane	250–260	180	(69)
22. 4,4'-Dihydroxy-3,3',5,5'-tetrabromo-diphenyl-2,2-propane	240–260	157	(69)
23. 4,4'-Dihydroxy-diphenyl-2,2-butane	205–222	134	(27,62)
24. 4,4'-Dihydroxy-diphenyl-2,2-pentane	200–220	137	(27,69)
25. 4,4'-Dihydroxy-diphenyl-2,2-(4-methyl pentane)	200–220	...	(27)

TABLE III-6 (*continued*)

Polycarbonate from	Melting range [°C]	Second-order transition temp. [°C]	Reference
26. 4,4'-Dihydroxy-diphenyl-2,2-*n*-hexane	180–200	. . .	(27)
27. 4,4'-Dihydroxy-diphenyl-2,2-nonane	170–190	. . .	(27)
28. 4,4'-Dihydroxy-diphenyl-4,4-heptane	190–200	148	(27,69)
29. 4,4'-Dihydroxy-diphenyl phenyl methyl methane	210–230	176	(27,69)
30. 4,4'-Dihydroxy-diphenyl-4-chlorophenyl methyl methane	203	. . .	(81)
31. 4,4'-Dihydroxy-diphenyl-2,5-dichlorophenyl methyl methane	244	. . .	(81)
32. 4,4'-Dihydroxy-diphenyl-3,4-dichlorophenyl methyl methane	197–244	. . .	(81,85)
33. 4,4'-Dihydroxy-diphenyl-4-fluorophenyl methyl methane	201	. . .	(82)
34. 4,4'-Dihydroxy-diphenyl-2-naphthyl methyl methane	188	. . .	(80)
35. 4,4'-Dihydroxy-tetraphenyl methane	210–230	121	(69)
36. 4,4'-Dihydroxy-diphenyl phenyl cyanomethane	210–225	138	(62)
37. 4,4'-Dihydroxy-diphenyl-1,2-ethane	290–300	. . .	(27)
38. 4,4'-Dihydroxy-diphenyl-1,10-*n*-decane	135–150	. . .	(62)
39. 4,4'-Dihydroxy-diphenyl-1,6-(1,6-dioxo-*n*-hexane)	225	. . .	(62)
40. 4,4'-Dihydroxy-diphenyl-1,10-(1,10-dioxo-*n*-decane)	160–175	. . .	(62)
41. 4,4'-Dihydroxy-diphenyl ether	230–235	145	(69)
42. Bis-*p*-hydroxy-phenyl-ether-4,4'-diphenyl	250	. . .	(120)
43. 4,4'-Dihydroxy-diphenyl sulfide	220–240	113	(69)
44. 4,4'-Dihydroxy-3,3'-dimethyl diphenyl sulfide	190–200	67	. . .
45. 4,4'-Dihydroxy-diphenyl sulfoxide	230–250	173	(69)
46. 4,4'-Dihydroxy-diphenyl sulfone	200–210	. . .	(69)
47. 4,4'-Dihydroxy-3,3'-dichlorodiphenyl sulfone	274–276	. . .	. . .
48. $\alpha,\alpha,\alpha',\alpha'$-Tetramethyl-$\alpha,\alpha'$-(di-*p*-hydroxyphenyl)-*p*-xylylene	230–250	162	. . .
49. $\alpha,\alpha,\alpha',\alpha'$-Tetramethyl-$\alpha,\alpha'$-(di-*p*-hydroxyphenyl)-*m*-xylylene	210–230	120	. . .
50. 2,2'-Dihydroxy-3,3',5,5'-tetramethyl-diphenyl methane	220–230	137	. . .

TABLE III-7

Polycarbonate Copolymers from Various Aromatic Dihydroxy Compounds

Polycarbonate copolymer from		Melting range [°C]	Second order transition temperature [°C]	Reference
Component A (mole %)	Component B (mole %)			
1. 4,4'-Dihydroxy-diphenyl-2,2-propane 0.95	4,4'-Dihydroxy-diphenyl-1,1-cyclohexane 0.05	205	...	(28)
2. " 0.9	Bis-(4-hydroxy-3-carboxylic acid phenyl ester phenyl) methane 0.1	200–210	...	(14)
3. " 0.1	4,4'-Dihydroxy-diphenyl-2,2-butane 0.9	210–220	138	...
4. " 0.8	1,6-(4,4'-Dihydroxy-diphenyl)-1,6-dioxohexane 0.2	175–190	109	...
5. " 0.9	Hydroquinone 0.1	225–240	...	(70)
" 0.8	0.2	238–245	...	(70)
6. " 0.5	Resorcinol 0.5	210–215	132	...
7. " 0.6	4,4'-Dihydroxy-diphenyl 0.4	265–270	...	(70)
" 0.5	0.5	270–275	172	...
8. " 0.8	1,6-Dihydroxy-naphthalene 0.2	240–260	150	(70)

No.	Component 1		Component 2				
9.	"	0.9	2,6-Dihydroxy-naphthalene	0.1	290	162	...
	"	0.8		0.2	300	156	...
10.	"	0.9	3,5-Dihydroxy-benzoic acid ethyl ester	0.1	200–210	...	(114)
11.	4,4'-Dihydroxy-diphenyl-2,2-propane	0.75	4,4'-Dihydroxy-diphenyl ether	0.25	170–228	...	(75)
		0.5		0.5	155–210	...	(75)
12.	"	0.55	4,4'-Dihydroxy-diphenyl ether	0.45	163–187	...	(75)
13.	"	0.5	4,4'-Dihydroxy-diphenyl sulfide	0.5	185–203	125	(72)
14.	"	0.8	4,4'-Dihydroxy-diphenyl sulfone	0.2	280–285	154	...
		0.6		0.4	250–252	179	...
		0.5		0.5	245–255	179	...
15.	4,4'-Dihydroxy-diphenyl-2,2-butane	0.8	4,4'-Dihydroxy-diphenyl ether	0.2	205–225	...	(72)
16.	Hydroquinone	0.15	4,4'-Dihydroxy-diphenyl ether	0.85	208	...	(75)
17.	Dihydroxy-diphenyl	0.25	4,4'-Dihydroxy-diphenyl ether	0.75	210–238	...	(75)
18.	4,4'-Dihydroxy-benzophenone	0.5	4,4'-Dihydroxy-diphenyl ether	0.75	250–263	...	(75)
19.	4,4'-Dihydroxy-diphenyl sulfone	0.5	4,4'-Dihydroxy-diphenyl ether	0.5	175–215	...	(75)
20.	"	0.5	4,4'-Dihydroxy-3,3'-dimethyl diphenyl sulfone	0.5	240–260	174	...

tures into an insoluble crosslinked material, the physical properties of which can be improved by the use of glass fiber materials such as mats and woven and nonwoven fabrics (115). These products can be used as raw materials for surface coatings of the air and oven-baking type and also as casting or molding resins.

D. CROSSLINKING OF POLYCARBONATES BY THE ADDITION OF REACTIVE POLY-FUNCTIONAL COMPOUNDS. Crosslinked products may be obtained by heating mixtures of aromatic polycarbonates with hexamethylene tetra-mine, or paraformaldehyde (116) or with phenolaldehyde resins of the Novolak type to temperatures above 170°C. The phenolic resins can be added carefully at the relatively low temperature of transesterification of the aromatic dihydroxy compounds with diphenyl carbonate (117). Polyepoxy compounds are very good crosslinking agents for polycarbonates. If meltable aromatic or aliphatic polycarbonates or polycarbonate copolymers are mixed with polyepoxy compounds and the mixtures are heat-cured, colorless, transparent, insoluble, and unmeltable materials with good mechanical and electrical properties result (118). Polyepoxy compounds, such as polyethers from 4,4'-dihydroxy-diphenyl-2,2-propane and epichlorohydrin or 2,2-dicyclohexenyl propane dioxide and hardeners, such as dicarboxylic acid anhydrides or polyamines, may be used. These mixtures can be utilized as molding resins, raw materials for surface coatings, binders for laminates, and adhesives.

High molecular weight polycarbonate copolymers from aromatic di-hydroxy compounds, such as bisphenol A, and polyalkylene glycol ethers, as they can be obtained, e.g., by phosgenating mixtures of bis-phenol A and polyalkylene glycol ethers in pyridine which contain aromatic polyisocyanates such as tolylene diisocyanates, will crosslink on heating (119).

8. Compilation of the Most Important Polycarbonates and Polycarbonate Copolymers Prepared to Date

In Tables III-6, 7, and 8 the most important aromatic polycarbonates as well as polycarbonate copolymers from various aromatic and from aromatic and aliphatic dihydroxy compounds prepared to date are summarized. As a characterization, the melting range and the second-order transition point are given. The melting range of macromolecular substances is influenced by the molecular weight, the molecular structure, the state of crystallization in the test piece, and last but not least the test method used. Since the literature did not contain sufficient informa-

TABLE III-8
Polycarbonate Copolymers from Aromatic
and Aliphatic Dihydroxy Compounds

Polycarbonate copolymer from		Melting range [°C]	Second-order transition temp. [°C]	Reference
Component A (mole %)	Component B (mole %)			
1. 4,4'-Dihydroxy-diphenyl-2,2-propane	Ethylene glycol			
0.8	0.2	200–220	. . .	(86)
0.5	0.5	165–180	. . .	(86)
0.5	0.5	196–200	. . .	(70)
2. "	Butanediol-1,4			
0.5	0.5	190	. . .	(121)
3. "	Hexanediol-1,6			
0.8	0.2	165–190	94	(86)
0.7	0.3	180–210	. . .	(70)
0.5	0.5	220–240	. . .	(70)
4. "	4,4'-Dihydroxy-dicyclohexyl-2,2-propane			
0.8	0.2	205–230	. . .	(86)
0.5	0.5	190–210	. . .	(86)
0.5	0.5	255–257	161	(70)
5. "	p-Xylylene gly-col			
0.5	0.5	200–210		(70)
6. "	Polyethylene glycol $M = 4000$			
0.91	0.09	170–180	. . .	(86)
7. "	Polypropylene glycol $M = 2000$			
0.91	0.09	160–190	. . .	(86)
8. "	Polybutylene glycol $M = 1000$			
0.83	0.17	165–190	. . .	(86)
9. "	Diphenyl silane-diol			
0.7	0.3	170–180	. . .	(86)
10. 4,4'-Dihydroxy-diphenyl sulfone	1,6-Hexanediol			
0.3	0.7	32–45	. . .	(86)

TABLE III-8 *(continued)*

Polycarbonate copolymer from		Melting range [°C]	Second-order transition temp. [°C]	Reference
Component A (mole %)	Component B (mole %)			
11. 4,4'-Dihydroxy-diphenyl sulfone	Polyethylene glycol $M = 4000$			
0.9	0.1	170–185	...	(86)
12. Hydroquinone	Ethylene glycol			
0.5	0.5	200–220	...	(76)
13. "	1,6-Hexanediol			
0.5	0.5	150–170	...	(76)
14. "	4,4'-Dihydroxy-dicyclohexyl-2,2-propane			
0.5	0.5	270–275	...	(76)

tion on the above, the figures shown can be used only as preliminary information. The second-order transition temperature is much better defined, since it is determined by physically unobjectionable methods. However, second-order transition temperatures of comparable macromolecular substances may differ to some extent, depending on the physical method of determination used. For the evaluation of the second-order transition temperatures compiled in Table III-7 it is therefore important to consider the method of determination described in the cited literature.

References

1. Fr. Pat. 905,141 (1945), I. G. Farbenindustrie A. G.
2. S. Petersen in E. Müller, ed., *Methoden der Organischen Chemie, (Houben-Weyl) Vol. VIII/III,* 101ff. Georg Thieme-Verlag, Stuttgart, 1952.
3. E. Müller and O. Bayer (to Farbenfabriken Bayer A. G.), U. S. Pat. 2,999,844 (1961).
4. Ger. Pat. 109,933 (1900), Chemische Fabrik von Heyden, *Friedl.* **5,** 730 (1901); Ger. Pat. 116,386 (1900), Chemische Fabrik von Heyden, *Friedl.* **6,** 1160 (1904); Ger. Pats. 114,025, 117,624, 117,625, 118,536, 118,537, 118,566 (1900), Farbenfabriken vorm. Friedrich Bayer u. Comp., *Friedl.* **6,** 1161–1166 (1904).
5. Ch. Scholtissek, *Ber.* **89,** 2562 (1956).
6. Ger. Pat. 255,942 (1912), Farbenfabriken vorm. Friedrich Bayer u. Comp., *Friedl.* **11,** 115 (1915).
7. S. Sarel and L. A. Pohoryles, *J. Am. Chem. Soc.* **80,** 4596 (1958); S. Sarel, L. A. Pohoryles, and R. Ben-Shoshan, *J. Org. Chem.* **24,** 1873 (1959).

8. H. Krzikalla and K. Merkel (to Badische Anilin-und Sodafabrik A.G.), Ger. Pat. 857,948 (1952).
9. H. Willersinn (to Badische Anilin-und Sodafabrik A.G.), Ger. Pat. Appl. 1,100,952 (1961).
10. W. H. Carothers and F. J. van Natta, *J. Am. Chem. Soc.* **52**, 314 (1930); J. W. Hill and W. H. Carothers, *J. Am. Chem. Soc.* **55**, 5031 (1933).
11. H. C. Stevens (to Columbia-Southern Chem. Corp.), U. S. Pat. 2,787,632 (1952).
12. W. R. Peterson (to E. I. du Pont de Nemours & Co.), U. S. Pat. 2,210,817 (1940).
13. H. F. Piepenbrink in E. Müller, ed., *Methoden der Organischen Chemie, (Houben-Weyl) Vol. VIII/III,* 245, Georg Thieme-Verlag, Stuttgart, 1952.
14. M. Gawlak, R. P. Palmer, J. B. Rose, D. J. H. Sandiford, and A. Turner-Jones, *Chemistry and Industry* **25,** 1148 (1962).
15. D. D. Reynolds and J. Van Den Berghe (to Eastman Kodak Co.), U. S. Pat. 2,789,968 (1957).
16. H. C. Stevens (to Columbia-Southern Chem. Corp.), Brit. Pats. 820,603 (1959), 828,523 (1960), 828,524 (1960), 872,983 (1961).
17. J. W. Hill, *J. Am. Chem. Soc.* **57,** 1131 (1935).
18. D. D. Reynolds and J. Van Den Berghe (to Eastman Kodak Co.), U. S. Pat. 2,789,509 (1957).
19. J. L. R. Williams and K. R. Dunham (to Eastman Kodak Co.), U. S. Pat. 2,843,567 (1958).
20. D. D. Reynolds and J. Van Den Berghe (to Eastman Kodak Co.), U. S. Pat. 2,789,970 (1957).
21. D. D. Reynolds and K. R. Dunham (to Eastman Kodak Co.), U. S. Pat. 2,789,969 (1957).
22. D. D. Reynolds and K. R. Dunham (to Eastman Kodak Co.), U. S. Pat. 2,789,971 (1957).
23. D. D. Reynolds and J. Van Den Berghe (to Eastman Kodak Co.), U. S. Pats. 2,789,964, 2,789,965 (1957).
24. J. R. Caldwell (to Eastman Kodak Co.), U. S. Pat. 2,799,666 (1957).
25. H. Rinke, W. Lehmann, and H. Schnell (to Farbenfabriken Bayer A. G.), Ger. Pat. 1,050,544 (1959).
26. Belg. Pats. 576,465, 576,633 (1959), Solvay and Cie.
27. H. Schnell, *Angew. Chem.* **68,** 633 (1956).
28. H. Schnell, L. Bottenbruch, and H. Krimm (to Farbenfabriken Bayer A. G.), Ger. Pat. 971,790 (1959); Belg. Pat. 532,543 (1954).
29. N. I. Schirokova, E. F. Russkova, A. B. Alischoeva, R. M. Gitina, J. J. Levkojev, and P. V. Kozlov, *Vysokomolekul. Soedin.* **3,** No. 4, 642 (1961)·
30. Anon., *Chem. Eng.,* 174 (November 14, 1960).
31. I. Ugi and F. Beck, *Ber.* **94,** 1839 (1961).
32. A. Einhorn, *Ann.* **300,** 135 (1898).
33. W. W. Moyer, Jr., J. Wynstra, and J. S. Frey (to Union Carbide Corp.), U. S. Pat. 2,970,131 (1961).
34. J. J. Dietrich and H. C. Stevens (to Columbia-Southern Chem. Corp.), Belg. Pat. 579,605 (1959).
35. J. J. Dietrich, A. J. Kaman, and H. C. Stevens (to Columbia-Southern Chem. Corp.), Belg. Pat. 584,933 (1958).

36. L. Bottenbruch and H. Schnell (to Farbenfabriken Bayer A. G.), Ger. Pats. 959,497 (1957), 1,046,311 (1958); H. Schnell, *Angew. Chem.* **73,** 629 (1961).

37. A. J. Conix, (to Gevaert Photo Producten N.V.), Belg. Pat. 601,392 (1961).

38. H. Schnell, L. Bottenbruch, H. Schwarz, and H. G. Lotter (to Farbenfabriken Bayer A. G.), Belg. Pat. 603,106 (1961).

39. Belg. Pat. 592,065 (1960), 592,067 (1960), N. V. Onderzoekingsinstituut Research.

40. L. Bottenbruch and H. Schnell (to Farbenfabriken Bayer A. G.), Belg. Pat. 589,607 (1960); A. J. Jakubovič et al., U. S. S. R. Pat. 132,402 (1960).

41. N. Melnikov, *J. Prakt. Chem.* **128,** 233 (1931).

42. A. Conix, *Ind. Chim. Belge* **22,** 1457 (1957); W. M. Eareckson, *J. Polymer Sci.* **40,** 399 (1959); J. P. Losey et al., *Vysokomolekul. Soedin.* **2,** 1659 (1960).

43. F. Schimke, Diss. Berlin, 1961; *J. Prakt. Chem.* [4] **17,** 107 (1962); Belg. Pat. 617,358 (1962), VEB Filmfabrik Agfa Wolfen.

44. Jap. Pat. Appl. Publ. No. 4542 (1961), Kunoshima Kagaku Kogyo K. K.

45. D. E. Darr and R. P. Naworski (to Columbia-Southern Chem. Corp.), Belg. Pat. 581,113 (1959); (to Pittsburgh Plate Glass Co.), Belg. Pat. 606,885 (1962).

46. J. J. Dietrich and R. D. Swigert (to Columbia-Southern Chem. Corp.), Belg. Pat. 579,572 (1959).

47. R. D. Swigert et al. (to Columbia-Southern Chem. Corp.), Belg. Pats. 579,569–571 (1959).

48. D. E. Darr and R. P. Naworsky (to Columbia-Southern Chem. Corp.), Belg. Pat. 583,766 (1959).

49. Belg. Pat. 577,552 (1959), N. V. Onderzoekingsinstituut Research.

50. L. Bottenbruch and H. Schnell (to Farbenfabriken Bayer A. G.), Belg. Pat. 577,943 (1959).

51. H. Schnell and K. H. Fritsch (to Farbenfabriken Bayer A. G.), Belg. Pat. 589,144 (1960).

52. Jap. Pat. Appls. 15,598, 16,250 (1958), Kunoshima Kagaku Kogyo K. K.

53. C. A. Bischoff and A. v. Hedenstroem, *Ber.* **35,** 3431 (1902).

54. Brit. Pat. 839,858 (1960), General Electric Co.

55. J. v. Braun, *Ann.* **472,** 1 (1929).

56. A. Y. Yakubovich, G. Y. Gordon, L. I. Maslennikova, E. M. Grobman, K. I. Trat'yakova, and N. I. Kokoreva, *J. Polymer Sci.* **55,** 251 (1961).

57. R. Fosse, *Compt. rend.* **136,** 1074 (1903); P. D. Ritchie, *J. Chem. Soc. (London),* 1054 (1935).

58. Jap. Pat. Appl. Publ. No. 694 (1961), Kunoshima Kagaku Kogyo K. K.

59. Brit. Pat. 882,540 (1961), Kunoshima Kagaku Kogyo K. K.

60. I. P. Losev, O. V. Smirnova, and E. V. Smurova, *Vysokomolekul. Soedin.* **2,** 1665 (1960).

61. H. Schnell and G. Fritz (to Farbenfabriken Bayer A. G.), Ger. Pat. 1,031,512 (1958).

62. H. Schnell, *The Plastics Institute, Transaction and Journal* **28,** 143 (1960).

63. H. Schnell and G. Fritz (to Farbenfabriken Bayer A. G.), Ger. Pats. 1,020,184 (1958), 1,024,710 (1958).

64. H. A. Staab, *Ann.* **609,** 75 (1957); *Angew. Chem.* **68,** 754 (1956).

65. H. Staab and F. Ebel (to Badische Anilin-und Sodafabrik A. G.), Fr. Pat. 1,208,196 (1960); Fr. Pat. 1,202,915 (1960), P. Beiersdorf u. Co. A. G.

66. M. Sander, Ger. Pat. 1,067,213 (1960).
67. W. Sweeny, *J. Appl. Polymer Sci.* **5,** No. 16, 15 (1961).
68. H. Schnell and L. Bottenbruch, *Die Makrom. Chem.* **57,** 1 (1962).
69. H. Schnell, *Ind. Eng. Chem.* **51,** 157 (1959).
70. H. Schnell, L. Bottenbruch, H. Krimm, and G. Fritz (to Farbenfabriken Bayer A. G.), Ger. Pat. 971,777 (1959).
71. H. Schnell, H. Krimm, and L. Bottenbruch (to Farbenfabriken Bayer A. G.), Ger. Pat. 1,007,996 (1957).
72. H. Schnell and H. Krimm (to Farbenfabriken Bayer A. G.), Belg. Pat. 560,610 (1957).
73. H. Schnell and H. Krimm (to Farbenfabriken Bayer A. G.), U. S. Pat. 2,999,846 (1961).
74. H. Schnell and L. Bottenbruch (to Farbenfabriken Bayer A. G.), Ger. Pat. 1,045,657 (1958).
75. D. W. Fox (to General Electric Co.), Belg. Pat. 570,529 (1958).
76. H. Schnell, W. Kimpel, L. Bottenbruch, H. Krimm, and G. Fritz (to Farbenfabriken Bayer A. G.), Ger. Pat. 1,011,148 (1959).
77. L. Bottenbruch, G. Fritz, and H. Schnell (to Farbenfabriken Bayer A. G.), Belg. Pat. 568,545 (1958).
78. T. M. Laakso and D. A. Buckley (to Kodak S. A.), Belg. Pat. 591,169 (1960).
79. T. M. Laakso and D. A. Buckley (to Kodak S. A.), Belg. Pat. 591,970 (1960).
80. T. M. Laakso and D. A. Buckley (to Kodak S. A.), Belg. Pat. 593,040 (1960).
81. T. M. Laakso and M. C. Petropoulos (to Kodak S. A.), Belg. Pat. 593,041 (1960).
82. T. M. Laakso, D. A. Buckley, and M. C. Petropoulos (to Kodak S. A.), Belg. Pat. 593,042 (1960).
83. T. M. Laakso and D. A. Buckley (to Kodak S. A.), Belg. Pat. 593,043 (1960).
84. T. M. Laakso and D. A. Buckley (to Kodak S. A.), Belg. Pat. 593,045 (1960).
85. T. M. Laakso and M. C. Petropoulos (to Kodak S. A.), Belg. Pat. 593,046 (1960).
86. E. P. Goldberg (to Compagnie Francaise Thomson Houston), Fr. Pat. 1,198,715 (1959).
87. Ger. Pat. Appl. I76,493 (1943), I. G. Farbenindustrie A. G.
88. H. C. Stevens (to Columbia-Southern Chem. Corp.), Belg. Pat. 581,249 (1960).
89. S. H. Merrill (to Kodak S. A.), Belg. Pat. 593,044 (1960); S. H. Merrill, *J. Polymer Sci.* **55,** 343 (1961).
90. D. D. Reynolds and K. R. Dunham (to Eastman Kodak Co.), U. S. Pats. 2,789,966; 2,789,972 (1957).
91. E. P. Goldberg (to General Electric Co.), Belg. Pats. 570,530; 570,531 (1958); U. S. Pat. 3,030,331 (1962), General Electric Co.
92. Fr. Pat. 1,177,517 (1959), Chem. Werke Albert; B. E. Jennings (to Imperial Chemical Industries Ltd.), Brit. Pat. 897,640 (1962).
93. Belg. Pat. 576,464 (1959), Solvay and Cie.
94. Belg. Pat. 575,874 (1959), Inventa A. G.
95. V. Böllert, H. Schnell, and G. Fritz (to Farbenfabriken Bayer A. G.), Belg. Pat. 595,996 (1960).
96. H. Schnell, V. Böllert, and G. Fritz (to Farbenfabriken Bayer A. G.), Belg. Pat. 597,654 (1960).

97. M. L. Clachan, N. S. McPherson, K. R. Tatchell, and T. A. Abott (to Bexford Ltd.), U. S. Pat. 3,000,849 (1961).

98. J. R. Caldwell (to Eastman Kodak Co.), U. S. Pat. 2,808,390 (1957).

99. W. E. Bissinger, F. Strain, H. C. Stevens, W. R. Dial, and R. S. Chisholm (to Columbia-Southern Chem. Corp.), Belg. Pat. 573,065 (1959).

100. Belg. Pat. 576,389 (1959), Bexford Ltd.

101. V. S. Foldi and T. W. Campbell, *J. Polymer Sci.* **56,** 1 (1962).

102. Brit. Pat. 845,650 (1960), Chem. Werke Albert.

103. E. P. Goldberg (to General Electric Co.), U. S. Pat. 2,999,845 (1961).

104. K. B. Goldblum (to General Electric Co.), Belg. Pat. 570,525 (1959).

105. A. A. Miller, E. J. Lawton, and J. S. Balwitt, *J. Polymer Sci.* **14,** 503 (1954); F. A. Bovey, *"The Effects Of Ionizing Radiation On Natural And Synthetic High Polymers," Polymer Reviews, Vol. I.* Interscience, New York, 1958.

106. R. Harrington and R. Giberson, *Mod. Plastics* **36,** 199 (November 1958); R. C. Giberson, *Mod. Plastics* **39,** 143 (April 1962).

107. H. Schnell, U. Veiel, and L. Bottenbruch (to Farbenfabriken Bayer A. G.), Belg. Pat. 580,212 (1959).

108. R. E. Barker, Jr., and W. G. Moulton, *J. Polymer Sci.* **47,** 175 (1960).

109. D. G. Borden, C. C. Unruh, and S. H. Merrill (to Kodak S. A.), Belg. Pat. 593,169 (1960).

110. W. Thoma and H. Rinke (to Farbenfabriken Bayer A. G.), Ger. Pat. Appl. 1,099,732 (1961).

111. E. P. Goldberg (to General Electric Co.), Belg. Pat. 570,528 (1959).

112. E. P. Goldberg (to General Electric Co.), Belg. Pat. 570,527 (1959).

113. H. Schnell and H. Krimm (to Farbenfabriken Bayer A. G.), Ger. Pat. Appl. 1,108,433 (1961).

114. L. Bottenbruch and H. Schnell (to Farbenfabriken Bayer A. G.), Ger. Pat. 1,086,885 (1961).

115. H. Schnell and W. Schulte-Huermann (to Farbenfabriken Bayer A. G.), Ger. Pat. 1,031,965 (1958); T. F. Bradley and R. T. Holm (to Bataafsche Petroleum Mij.), Belg. Pat. 577,624 (1959).

116. K. B. Goldblum (to General Electric Co.), U. S. Pat. 3,014,891 (1961).

117. K. B. Goldblum (to General Electric Co.), U. S. Pat. 2,950,266 (1959).

118. H. Schnell and H. Krimm (to Farbenfabriken Bayer A. G.), Ger. Pat. Appl. 1,113,085 (1961).

119. E. P. Goldberg (to General Electric Co.), U. S. Pat. 3,030,335 (1962).

120. D. W. Fox (to General Electric Co.), Belg. Pat. 559,191 (1957).

121. H. Goelz and F. Meyer (to Badische Anilin-und Sodafabrik A. G.), Brit. Pat. 843, 314 (1960).

IV. THE PRODUCTION OF THE MOST IMPORTANT RAW MATERIALS AND INTER-MEDIATES FOR AROMATIC POLYCARBONATES

This chapter is devoted to the production of 4,4′-dihydroxy-diphenyl methane derivatives and diphenyl carbonate. Other intermediates for aromatic polycarbonates, such as dihydroxy-diaryl ethers, sulfides, or sulfones, have not been considered since they have not yet attained commercial significance. Nor has any consideration been given to the generation and purification of phosgene, a subject treated at length elsewhere.

1. DERIVATIVES OF 4,4′-DIHYDROXY-DIARYL METHANE

4,4′-Dihydroxy-diphenyl methane as well as a large number of derivatives of this compound have been known to chemists for many years. Some of them, featuring alkyl groups attached to the aromatic groups, are used as color-stable antioxidants for natural and synthetic rubbers, polyvinyls, and mineral oils (1).

Derivatives of 4,4′-dihydroxy-diphenyl methane have furthermore been suggested for, and to some extent found actual application in, the manufacture of phenolic resins and tanning agents. A number of derivatives of 4,4′-dihydroxy-diphenyl methane have specific physiological effects. For example, 4,4′-dihydroxy-diphenyl-2,2-propane (bisphenol A) is an estrogen (2). Others are effective against coccidiosis in poultry (3). Quinoline or isoquinoline attached to the central carbon atom of 4,4′-dihydroxy-diphenyl methane compounds results in products exhibiting laxative properties (4).

Since 1938 the epoxy resins based on bisphenol A and epichlorohydrin have been developed (5) and found application in the fields of coatings, adhesives, and castable and moldable plastics. The commercial production of large quantities of bisphenol A soon became a necessity. However, the epoxy resins did not require bisphenol A of exceptional purity. The development of the aromatic polycarbonates presented the necessity of producing this intermediate with a degree of purity sufficient for building up a high molecular weight polyester. To date, commercial aromatic polycarbonates are produced almost exclusively on the basis of bisphenol A. As compared to other aromatic dihydroxy compounds, bisphenol A is preferred because of the relative ease with which it is produced from widely available and economical raw materials (phenol and acetone). Other derivatives of 4,4′-dihydroxy-diphenyl methane will yield poly-carbonates having different, sometimes better, properties.

Further commercial development of the aromatic polycarbonates will therefore be strongly influenced by the discovery of new economical processes for making 4,4′-dihydroxy-diphenyl methane derivatives other than bisphenol A, and it is for this reason that in the following para-graphs the present state of technology in the field of manufacturing these compounds is presented (6).

A. Production of Dihydroxy-Diaryl Methane Derivatives from Aromatic Hydroxy Compounds and Aldehydes or Ketones

Dihydroxy-diaryl alkanes are formed by condensing aromatic hydroxy compounds with aldehydes or ketones under the influence of alkaline or acidic condensation catalysts.

Acidic catalysts are usually preferred, since they are effective at lower temperatures and thus yield fewer by-products.

1. Reaction of Aromatic Hydroxy Compounds with Carbonyl Compounds in the Presence of Acidic Condensing Agents

The reaction of aromatic hydroxy compounds with carbonyl com-pounds leading to dihydroxy-diaryl methane derivatives is a condensation with water being separated.

$$(\text{IV-1}) \quad 2 \ \langle\!\!\!\bigcirc\!\!\!\rangle\!-\!\text{OH} \ + \ \overset{R}{\underset{R'}{\diagdown}}C\!=\!O \longrightarrow HO\!-\!\langle\!\!\!\bigcirc\!\!\!\rangle\!-\!\overset{\overset{R}{|}}{\underset{\underset{R'}{|}}{C}}\!-\!\langle\!\!\!\bigcirc\!\!\!\rangle\!-\!OH \ + \ H_2O$$

R, R′ = H, alkyl, or aryl

Unless the water is removed or tied up chemically, the reaction will come to a halt at a low-yield level. Acidic catalysts which have been employed are hydrogen chloride, hydrogen bromide, hydrogen fluoride, phosgene (7), boron fluoride, aluminum chloride, phosphorus halides, phosphorus pentoxide, phosphoric acid, concentrated hydrochloric acid, sulfuric acid, mixture of acetic acid with acetic anhydride, hydrogen chloride, or sulfuric acid, mixtures of hydrochloric and sulfuric acid, and cation exchange resins. Acidic substances which catalyze the reaction without at the same time acting as dehydrating agents will lead to high yields only if the water is removed by other means, such as, for example, azeotropic distillation with solvents or chemical reaction with $CaCl_2$ or P_2O_5.

4,4'-Dihydroxy-diphenyl methane, although having been produced earlier by a different route (8), was first obtained by reaction of phenol with formaldehyde in the presence of dilute mineral acids by Nölting and Herzberg (9); the yield was poor (10). The low temperature reactions of phenol with formaldehyde, paraformaldehyde, trioxane, or methylal in the presence of acidic condensing agents, such as concentrated hydrochloric acid, produce not only 4,4'-dihydroxy-diphenyl methane but also a number of other isomers, particularly the 2,2'- and 2,4'-forms, as well as resinous polycondensation products of the Novolak type. The formation of resins can be retarded by either using a large excess of phenol, calculated on formaldehyde, or carrying out the reaction in a homogeneous solution in dilute mineral acid. However, even at best the yield of 4,4'-dihydroxy-diphenyl methane is only about 35% (11); that of all isomers is 70%, calculated on phenol.

Other aliphatic and aromatic aldehydes, such as acetaldehyde, n-butyraldehyde, isobutyraldehyde, chloral (12), pyridine aldehyde (13), and benzaldehyde (14) can also be condensed with phenol in the presence of acidic condensing agents, such as concentrated hydrochloric acid or up to 70% sulfuric acid, sometimes with better yields of dihydroxy-diphenyl methane derivatives.

Considerably better yields of specific dihydroxy-diphenyl methane derivatives are obtained in the acidic condensation of 4-, 2,3-, 2,4-, 2,5-, 2,6-, 2,4,5-, and 2,3,4,6-substituted phenols with formaldehyde or other aldehydes (15).

Unsaturated aldehydes, such as acroleine, react with phenol at low temperatures in the presence of acidic condensing agents to form dihydroxy-diphenyl alkenes. At temperatures around 100°C these alkenes combine with additional phenol at the double bond, so that either tri- or polyphenols can be obtained, depending on the molar ratio of phenol to unsaturated aldehyde (16).

As compared to the aldehydes, ketones will condense with aromatic hydroxy compounds in the presence of acidic condensing agents with a better yield of specific condensation products. Of the aforementioned condensing agents, hydrogen chloride, concentrated hydrochloric acid, and up to 70% sulfuric acid are generally preferred. Concentrated sulfuric acid is even more effective but is unsuitable because of its tendency to sulfonate both the aromatic hydroxy compounds and the bisphenols obtained. Sulfuric acid of 70% or less concentration is not so effective as concentrated hydrochloric acid, which in turn is second to anhydrous hydrogen chloride. To date, other acidic condensing agents, such as BF_3-formic acid with calcium chloride as water acceptor (17), or cation exchange resins, such as sulfonated crosslinked polystyrenes (18), have not found commercial acceptance.

Among the ketones acetone (10) and alicyclic ketones, such as cyclohexanone (19), are the most reactive. In the dialkyl ketones the reactivity in condensation reactions decreases with increasing length of the alkyl chains (20). Condensation rates are even lower for alkyl-aryl ketones and diaryl ketones (21).

Ketocarboxylic acids, such as levulinic acid, can also be condensed with aromatic hydroxy compounds to form 4,4'-dihydroxy-diaryl alkanes carrying a carboxyl group attached to the alkyl group (22). Ketone mercaptals will condense much more readily than the ketones from which they are derived (23). Surprisingly, even acoyl cyanides, such as benzoyl cyanide, will condense with aromatic hydroxy compounds to bis-(4-hydroxyaryl)-aryl acetonitriles in the presence of highly acidic condensing agents (24).

The condensation is accelerated by catalytic amounts of ionizable compounds of divalent sulfur, such as sulfur dichloride, sodium thiosulfate, hydrogen sulfide, sodium sulfide, mercaptan, thiophenols, thioacetic acid, thioglycolic acid, mercaptoalkane sulfonic acids, or hydroxyalkyl mercaptans (25). Besides these sulfur compounds there are others which also have an accelerating effect, though not so pronounced: hydrogen selenide and hydrogen telluride (26), ferrous chloride (21), and acid soluble boron compounds, such as boric acid (27). Ultraviolet and gamma radiation also are reported to increase the rate of condensation (28).

In carrying out the condensation reaction, reactants may be introduced as pure substances or as solutions in inert solvents, such as aromatic hydrocarbons (29,30) chlorinated aliphatic hydrocarbons (31), acetic acid (10), etc.

In order to obtain a high yield of condensation products, the molar ratio of hydroxy compounds to ketones must be no less than 3.7 : 1 (32). The reaction should be carried out at the lowest reasonable temperature, certainly not above 65°C, since side reactions increase in magnitude with rising temperature (32,33).

Whenever the condensation is not carried out in solution, the reaction temperature has its lower limit at the point where the reactants no longer present a homogeneous liquid phase.

Many aromatic hydroxy compounds combine with ketones to form crystalline addition compounds having well-defined melting points (34).

4,4'-Dihydroxy-diphenyl-2,2-propane (bisphenol A) can be obtained by condensation of phenol with acetone in the presence of up to 70% sulfuric acid at temperatures below 70°C. To accelerate the condensation, mercaptan or mercaptocarboxylic acids are added. This process, however, produces a bisphenol A, which requires purification operations both extensive and high in losses before a sulfur-free refined product can be isolated.

The tightened purity specifications for bisphenol A have recently brought about a preference for the use of hydrogen chloride if the condensation is carried out in an inert solvent or concentrated hydrochloric acid as condensing agents (35). Besides bisphenol A (I) the acidic condensation of phenol with acetone produces a number of by-products which have not yet been positively identified. It is assumed, that these by-products include different isomers, such as 2,4'-dihydroxy-diphenyl-2,2-propane (II), trisphenols, such as 2,4-di-(4-hydroxycumyl)-phenol (III), and chroman derivatives, such as 2-methyl-2-(4-hydroxyphenyl)-4,4-dimethyl chroman (IV), and 2,2-dimethyl-4-methyl-4-(4-hydroxyphenyl)-chroman (V) (36), besides small amounts of isopropyl phenol, p-(1-methyl-vinyl)-phenol, and resinous by-products (see formula IV-2). The quality of by-products depends on reaction conditions and may run as high as 40% or more, with the isomers representing the largest portion. As the condensation temperature rises the quantity of by-products also goes up.

The quantity of unwanted isomers can be reduced substantially by selecting the condensation conditions in such a way, that either the bisphenol A itself or its addition compound with 1 mole of phenol crystallizes from the reaction mixture (37).

If the condensation is carried out in a saturated solution of phenol in concentrated hydrochloric acid, from which the addition compound of bisphenol A and phenol is precipitated in crystalline form at the same rate as it is produced, bisphenol A containing less than 2% of by-products can be obtained (38).

Since acids will split cumene hydroperoxide into phenol and acetone, it is possible to obtain bisphenol A directly by treating cumene hydroperoxide with acids, such as hydrogen chloride or concentrated hydrochloric acid. In order to achieve the desired molar ratio between the reactants, acetone may be distilled off or phenol added (39).

To obtain the 4,4'-dihydroxy-diaryl alkanes as refined finished goods, the reaction mixtures must be neutralized and all unreacted components, by-products, and solvents removed. The most direct method would be to neutralize the mineral acids with caustic or, better yet, sodium carbonate or bicarbonate solutions, which do not dissolve phenol and dihydroxy-diaryl alkanes, and, after washing out the electrolyte, to separate the organic phase by fractional distillation under vacuum (40). This method, however, is unsatisfactory, since at high temperatures the dihydroxy-diaryl alkanes are decomposed into alkenyl phenols and phenols, greatly accelerated by traces of alkaline impurities and/or metal ions, and furthermore the isomers cannot be separated by distillation.

The thermal decomposition of the dihydroxy-diaryl alkanes can be largely prevented by the use of stabilizing additives, particularly those capable of rendering alkaline impurities ineffective and tying up metal ions, such as the *sec.* and *tert.* alkaline earth phosphates (41).

Only a small purification effect is achieved by the process of first removing all unreacted starting materials from the condensation product, e.g., by a steam distillation, and then dissolving it in caustic alkali solution from which the product is recovered by an acid precipitation (42). A somewhat higher purity can be obtained by dissolving the condensation product in boiling dilute caustic alkali solution containing only about $^1/_{20}$ the theoretical equivalent of alkali required to neutralize the aromatic hydroxyl groups and recrystallizing by cooling (43). A disadvantage common to both methods is the fact that in an alkaline environment the dihydroxy-diphenyl alkanes are sensitive to atmospheric oxygen.

The gentlest purification method known is the recrystallization of the dihydroxy-diaryl alkanes or their addition products with aromatic hydroxy compounds from organic solvents, such as benzene, toluene, chlorotoluene, or dichloroethylene. By going through several recrystallization cycles, 4,4'-dihydroxy-diaryl alkanes can be isolated with a very high degree of purity. Phenol is also suitable as a solvent inasmuch as the addition products of phenol and the 4,4'-dihydroxy-diaryl alkanes crystallize well and are easily precipitated by lowering the solution temperature (44).

Better yet is recrystallization from phenol-water mixtures, which yields the above addition products in a very pure form (37).

The 4,4'-dihydroxy-diaryl alkanes are subsequently best recovered from the phenol addition compounds by simply distilling off the phenol.

A process has also been suggested for the extraction of the condensation product with some solvent capable of dissolving the by-products but not the 4,4'-dihydroxy-diaryl alkanes, e.g., heptane (45,46).

2. Reaction of Aromatic Hydroxy Compounds with Oxo Compounds in the Presence of Alkaline Condensing Agents

As compared to acidic condensation processes, the alkaline condensation of aromatic hydroxy compounds with carbonyl compounds to obtain dihydroxy-diaryl methane derivatives is of small practical significance.

The reaction of unsubstituted aromatic hydroxy compounds with formaldehyde in an alkaline environment produces mixtures of mono- and poly-(hydroxymethyl)-substituted aromatic hydroxy compounds from which specific substances are impossible or very difficult to isolate.

These hydroxymethyl phenols react further to form resols (47). In the process of resol formation dihydroxy-diaryl methane derivatives appear among other intermediate products.

Reasonable yields of dihydroxy-diphenyl methane derivatives are obtained from reactions involving 2,4- or 2,6-dialkylene-substituted phenols dissolved in aliphatic or aromatic aldehydes, under the influence of alkali metal hydroxides as condensing agents (48). Furthermore, nonsymmetrical dihydroxy-diphenyl methane derivatives are accessible by alkaline condensation of hydroxymethyl-substituted aromatic hydroxy compounds (e.g., produced from disubstituted phenols, such as 2,4-dimethyl phenol) with other 2,4- or 2,6-disubstituted phenols (49).

The alkaline condensation of aromatic hydroxy compounds with aldehydes is carried out in the absence of water at temperatures up to 130°C, frequently in an aliphatic alcohol solution. The condensation of saturated ketones, such as acetone, cyclohexanone, and acetophenone, with phenol or 2,4- or 2,6-disubstituted phenols at temperatures between 100 and 200°C, using alkali- or alkaline-earth-phenolate catalysts, produces dihydroxy-diphenyl methane derivatives at high-yield levels. Again, an excess of the aromatic hydroxy compound (3–7 moles per mole of ketone) favors bisphenol formation. The quantity of alkali- or alkaline-earth phenolates used should be no less than 1 mole nor more than 2.5 moles per mole of ketone. Larger quantities will increase the amount of resinous by-products (50).

The disadvantages of this process are the high-reaction temperatures (160–180°C) and the relatively long reaction times, both of which increase the dangers inherent in the sensitivity of phenols and bisphenols to oxidation in an alkaline environment. From the reaction mixtures the condensation products may be isolated by neutralizing with mineral acids, washing the organic phase, distilling off excess phenol, and crystallizing the crude bisphenol from aromatic hydrocarbon solutions.

B. Other Methods for the Preparation of 4,4′-Dihydroxy-Diphenyl Methane Derivatives

Another possible method of preparing 4,4′-dihydroxy-diaryl alkanes is the reaction of alkenyl phenols, such as p-vinyl-phenol, p-(2-methyl-vinyl)-phenol, p-(1-methyl-vinyl)-phenol, or p-(1-phenyl-vinyl)-phenol with aromatic hydroxy compounds, using small amounts of acidic or alkaline catalysts (51).

If acidic catalysts, such as hydrogen chloride, BF_3, or cation exchangers are used, the reactions proceed at satisfactory rates at or below room temperature. With alkaline catalysts, such as alkali phenolates or alkali carbonates, higher temperatures (100–160°C) are required. The particular advantages of this process are that only catalytic amounts of acidic or alkaline substances are needed, that the reaction takes place in an anhydrous system, and that nonsymmetrical 4,4'-dihydroxy-diaryl alkanes are quite easily obtained.

In the presence of strong mineral acids 4,4'-dihydroxy-diaryl alkanes are also formed by a reaction of phenols with unsaturated compounds capable of combining at the particular reaction conditions with aromatic hydroxy compounds to form at first alkenyl-substituted hydroxy aromatics. Unsaturated compounds of this group are halogen alkenes, such as 2-chloropropene or 1-chlorocyclohexene (52), olefines, such as propadiene or methyl acetylene (53), or enol esters, such as isopropenyl acetate (54).

The reaction of phenol with acetylene in the presence of acidic catalysts produces a good yield of 4,4'-dihydroxy-diphenyl-1,1-ethane (55).

C. Summary of the Most Important 4,4'-Dihydroxy-Diphenyl Methane Derivatives Produced to Date

Table IV-1 contains a summary of the most important 4,4'-dihydroxy-diphenyl methane derivatives which have been prepared to date. Each is characterized by its melting or freezing point. The boiling points cannot be used for this purpose, since these substances can be distilled only under high vacuum and then will often partially decompose.

Table IV-2 lists a number of aromatic dihydroxy compounds which do not properly belong in the dihydroxy-diphenyl methane derivative series, yet on a laboratory scale have yielded polycarbonates with advantageous properties.

The column "Uses" indicates those fields of application that were either suggested by the authors or have subsequently become known.

TABLE IV-1

Summary of the Most Important 4,4'-Dihydroxy-Diphenyl
Alkane Derivatives Produced to Date

4,4'-Dihydroxy-diphenyl alkane derivative	Melting point [°C]	Uses*	Reference
4,4'-Dihydroxy-diphenyl methane	163	B, C	(8,9,56)
" -3,3'-dimethyl-diphenyl methane	127	A	(57)
" -2,2'-dimethyl-diphenyl methane	163	A	(58)
" -3,3',5,5'-tetramethyl-diphenyl methane	175	A, D	(59)
" -3,3'-dichloro-diphenyl methane	185	B	. . .
" -3,3'-dimethoxy-diphenyl methane	108	A	(60)
" -2,2',5,5'-tetramethyl-diphenyl methane	182	A	(61)
" -2,2',3,3',5,5',6,6'-octamethyl-diphenyl methane	215	A	(62)
" -2,2'-dimethyl-5,5'-diisopropyl-diphenyl methane	163	A	(63)
" -2,2'-dimethyl-5,5'-dipropyl-diphenyl methane	150	A	(57)
" -2,2'-dimethyl-5,5'-di-*tert.*-butyl-diphenyl methane	179	A	(64)
" -3,3'-dimethyl-5,5'-di-*tert.*-butyl-diphenyl methane	103	A	(64)
" -3,3'-dimethyl-5,5'-dicarboxy-diphenyl methane	>290	B	(65)
" -diphenyl-1,1-ethane	123 b.p.$_1$ = 218	B, C	(66)
" -3,3'-dimethyl-diphenyl-1,1-ethane	128	A, D	(57)
" -3,3',5,5'-tetramethyl-diphenyl-1,1-ethane	145	A	(67)
" -2.2'-dimethyl-5,5'-diisopropyl-diphenyl-1,1-ethane	185	A	(68)
" -diphenyl-1,1-(2,2,2-trichloro)-ethane	212	B	(12)
" -3,3-di-*tert.*-butyl-diphenyl-1,1-ethane	201	A	(64)
" -diphenyl-1,1-propane	129	A	(57)
" -3,3'-dimethyl-diphenyl-1,1-propane	94	A	(57)
" -2,2'-dimethyl-diphenyl-1,1-propane	145	A	(57)
" -2,2'-dimethyl-5,5'-di-*tert.*-butyl-diphenyl-1,1-propane	190	A	(64)
" -diphenyl-1,1-butane	127	A, B	(66)
" -2,2'-dimethyl-diphenyl-1,1-butane	145	A	(57)

TABLE IV-1 (*continued*)

4,4'-Dihydroxy-diphenyl alkane derivative	Melting point [°C]	Uses*	Reference
4,4'-Dihydroxy-3,3'-dimethyl-diphenyl-1,1-butane	135	A	(57)
" -2,2',5,5'-tetramethyl-diphenyl-1,1-butane	172	A, D	(69)
" -2,2'-dimethyl-5,5'-di-*tert*.-butyl-diphenyl-1,1-butane	210	A	(70)
" -2,2'-dimethyl-5,5'-dibutyl-diphenyl-1,1-butane	122	A	(70)
" -2,2'-dimethyl-5,5'-di-*tert*.-pentyl-diphenyl-1,1-butane	163	A	(70)
" -diphenyl-1,1-isobutane	155	B	(71)
" -2,2'-dimethyl-5,5'-di-*tert*.-butyl-diphenyl-1,1-isobutane	229	A	(70)
" -diphenyl-1,1-pentane	128	A	(57)
" -2,2'-dimethyl-diphenyl-1,1-pentane	97	A	(57)
" -3,3'-dimethyl-diphenyl-1,1-pentane	149	A	(57)
" -diphenyl-1,1-hexane	111	A	(57)
" -2,2'-dimethyl-diphenyl-1,1-hexane	152	A	(57)
" -3,3'-dimethyl-diphenyl-1,1-hexane	78	A	(57)
" -2,2'-dimethyl-5,5'-di-*tert*.-butyl-diphenyl-1,1-(2-ethyl)-butane	197	A	(64)
" -diphenyl-1,1-heptane	120	A, B	(72)
" -2,2'-dimethyl-diphenyl-1,1-heptane	156	A	(57)
" -3,3'-dimethyl-diphenyl-1,1-heptane	85	A	(57)
" -3,3'-di-*tert*.-butyl-diphenyl-1,1-heptane	159	A	(64)
" -2,2'-dimethyl-5,5'-di-*tert*.-butyl-diphenyl-1,1-(3,4,4-trimethyl)-pentane	167	A	(64)
" -diphenyl-1,1-(2-cyclohexyl)-ethane	147	A	(73)
" -triphenyl methane	161	A, B, C	(74)
" -3,3',5,5'-tetramethyl-triphenyl methane	131	A	(67)

(*continued*)

TABLE IV-1 (*continued*)

4,4'-Dihydroxy-diphenyl alkane derivative	Melting point [°C]	Uses*	Reference
4,4'-Dihydroxy-2,2'-dimethyl-5,5'-di-*tert*.-butyl-triphenyl methane	200	A	(70)
" -diphenyl-2,5-dichloro-phenyl methane	...	B	(75)
" -diphenyl-2-chloro-phenyl methane	153	B	(76)
" -diphenyl-1-naphthyl methane	150	B	(77)
" -diphenyl-2-methoxy-phenyl methane	181	A	(78)
" -2,2'-dimethyl-5,5'-di-*tert*.-butyl-diphenyl-3,4-dimethoxy-phenyl methane	232	A	(70)
" -2,2'-dimethyl-5,5'-di-*tert*.-butyl-diphenyl-1,1-acetone	197	A, C	(70,79)
" -2,2'-dimethyl-5,5'-di-*tert*.-butyl-diphenyl-1,1-(2-methyl)-pentene-2,3	191	A	(70)
" -2,2'-dimethyl-5,5'-di-*tert*.-butyl-diphenyl-1,1-(2-methyl)-hexene-2,3	211	A	(70)
" -diphenyl-2,2-propane	156	A, B, C	(5,6,10,66,71)
" -3,3'-dimethyl-diphenyl-2,2-propane	136	A, B	(3)
" -3,3'-diisopropyl-diphenyl-2,2-propane	96	A, B	(3)
" -3,3'-diallyl-diphenyl-2,2-propane	b.p.$_{0.1}$ = 181–186	A, B	(3)
" -3,3'-diisobutyl-diphenyl-2,2-propane	90	A	(3)
" -3,3'-di-*tert*.-butyl-diphenyl-2,2-propane	114–115	C	(80)
" -3,3'-dimethoxy-diphenyl-2,2-propane	...	B	(81)
" -3,3'-dichloro-diphenyl-2,2-propane	91	B	(71)
" -3,3',5,5'-tetrachloro-diphenyl-2,2-propane	133	A, B, C	(82)
" -3,3',5,5'-tetrabromo-diphenyl-2,2-propane	...	B	(74,82)
" -3,3'-diphenyl-2,2-propane	99	A, B, C	(3)
" -diphenyl-2,2-butane	125	A, B	(83)
" -3,3'-dimethyl-diphenyl-2,2-butane	146	A	(83)

TABLE IV-1 (*continued*)

4,4'-Dihydroxy-diphenyl alkane derivative	Melting point [°C]	Uses*	Reference
4,4'-Dihydroxy-diphenyl-2,2-pentane	149	A, B	(84)
" -diphenyl-2,2-isopentane	194	A	(85)
" -diphenyl-2,2-hexane	...	A, B	(85)
" -diphenyl-2,2-isohexane	155	A, B	(86)
" -3,3'-dimethyl-diphenyl-2,2-(4-methyl)-pentane	129	A	(86)
" -diphenyl-2,2-heptane	101	A, B	(85)
" -diphenyl-2,2-octane	88	A, B, C	(85)
" -diphenyl-2,2-nonane	171	A, B	(71)
" -diphenyl-3,3-pentane	204	A, B	(85)
" -diphenyl-4,4-heptane	154	A, B	(85)
" -diphenyl-5,5-nonane	171	A	(85)
" -diphenyl-6,6-undecane	149	A	(85)
" -3,3'-diethyl-diphenyl-2,2-propane	b.p.$_{1.5}$ = 199–205		(71)
" -3,3'-dicyclohexyl-diphenyl-2,2-propane	145	B	(71)
" -3-methyl-diphenyl-2,2-propane	115	B	(71)
" :diphenyl-3,3-butanone-2	131	A	(87)
" -3,3'-dimethyl-diphenyl-3,3-butanone-2	157	A	(87)
" -diphenyl-4,4-hexanone-3	201	A	(88)
" -triphenyl-2,2,2-ethane	188	A, B, C	(85)
" -diphenyl-(4-chloro-phenyl) 2,2,2-ethane	...	B	(76)
" -diphenyl-(2,5-dichloro-phenyl)-2,2,2-ethane	...	B	(75)
" -diphenyl-(3,4-dichloro-phenyl)-2,2,2-ethane	...	B	(75)
" -diphenyl-(4-fluoro-phenyl)-2,2,2-ethane	...	B	(76)
" -diphenyl phenyl cyano-methane	208	B	(4)
" -diphenyl methyl *p*-toluyl methane	151	A	(84)
" -diphenyl methyl 4-methoxy-phenyl methane	245	A	(85)
" -tetraphenyl methane	286	A, B	(89)
" -triphenyl benzoyl methane	212	A	(90)
" -diphenyl dibenzyl methane	193	A	(85)
" -triphenyl-1,1,1-propane	180	A	(91)
" -diphenyl-4,4-valeric acid	173	A, C	(92)
" -diphenyl 4,4-valeric acid ester	...	...	(93)
" -diphenyl-1,1-cyclopentane	157	A, B	(84)

(*continued*)

TABLE IV-1 (*continued*)

4,4'-Dihydroxy-diphenyl alkane derivative	Melting point [°C]	Uses*	Reference
4,4'-Dihydroxy-diphenyl-1,1-cyclohexane	188	A, B, C	(86)
" -diphenyl-1,1-(3-methyl)-cyclo-hexane	167	A	(84)
" -diphenyl-1,1-(4-methyl)-cyclo-hexane	180	A	(84)
" -3,3',5,5'-tetrachloro-diphenyl-1,1-cyclohexane	149	B	(82)
" -3,3',5,5'-(tetraphenyl-ethyl)-diphenyl-1,1-cyclohexane	. . .	C	(94)
" -diphenyl-2,2-decaline	181	B	(71)

* Suitable for use:
  A = in the manufacture of epoxies
  B = in the manufacture of polycarbonates
  C = in the manufacture of other polyesters
  D = as stabilizers or antioxidants.

TABLE IV-2
Other Aromatic Dihydroxy Compounds Suitable for the Manufacture of Polycarbonate Resins

Aromatic dihydroxy compound	Melting point [°C]	Uses*	Reference
4,4'-Dihydroxy-diphenyl ether	162	B, C	(95)
" -diphenyl sulfide	152	B, C	(96)
" -3,3'-dimethyl-diphenyl sulfide	120	B	(96)
" -diphenyl sulfoxide	203	B	(97)
" -3,3'-dimethyl-diphenyl sulfoxide	190	B	(82)
" -diphenyl sulfone	240	B, C	(98)
" -3,3'-dimethyl-diphenyl sulfone	269	B	(82)
" -diphenyl-1,2-ethane	199	B, C	(99)
" -diphenyl-1,3-propane	108	C	(99)
" -diphenyl-1,4-butane	158	C	(99)
" -diphenyl-1,6-hexane	145	C	(99)
" -diphenyl-1,10-decane	140	B, C	(99)
" -diphenyl-1,10-(1,10-dioxo)-decane	212	B	(99)
" -diphenyl-1,6-(1,6-dioxo)-hexane	240	B	(99)
Bis-4,4'-(p-hydroxy-phenoxy)-diphenyl	243	B	(100)

* Suitable for use:
  A = in the manufacture of epoxies
  B = in the manufacture of polycarbonates
  C = in the manufacture of other polyesters
  D = as stabilizers or antioxidants.

2. DIPHENYL CARBONATE

The ester exchange process for the manufacture of aromatic polycarbonates (section III, 3, A, 4) calls for a diaryl carbonate as the carbonic acid ester carrier. Economic as well as process reasons have dictated the essentially exclusive use of diphenyl carbonate for this purpose.

Following are some of the reactions which have been suggested for the preparation of this compound:

(IV-4)

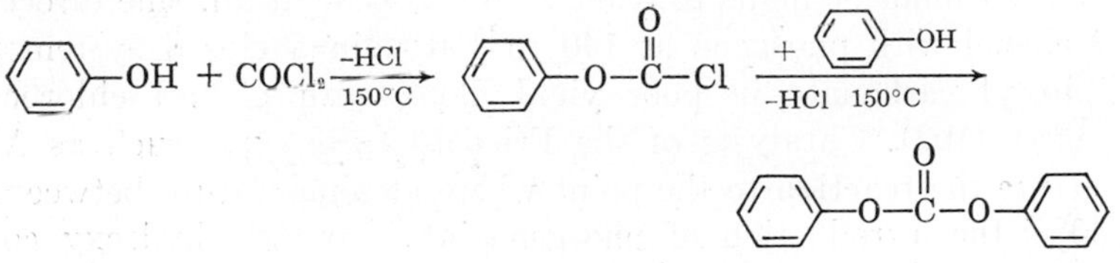

(IV-5)

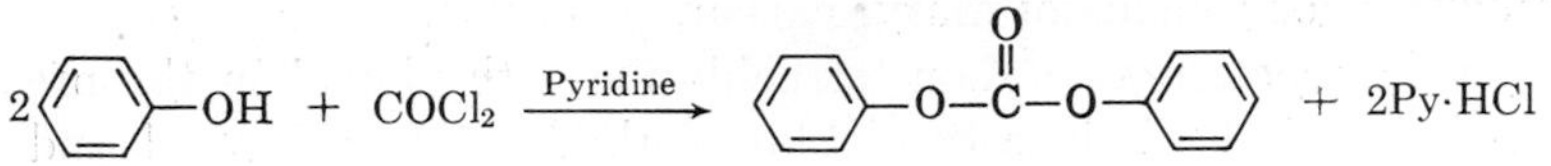

(IV-6)

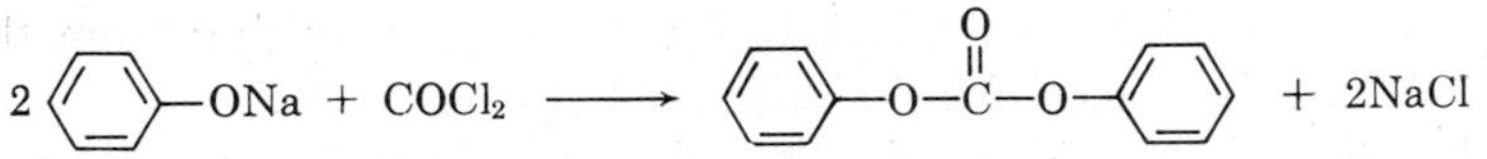

(IV-7)

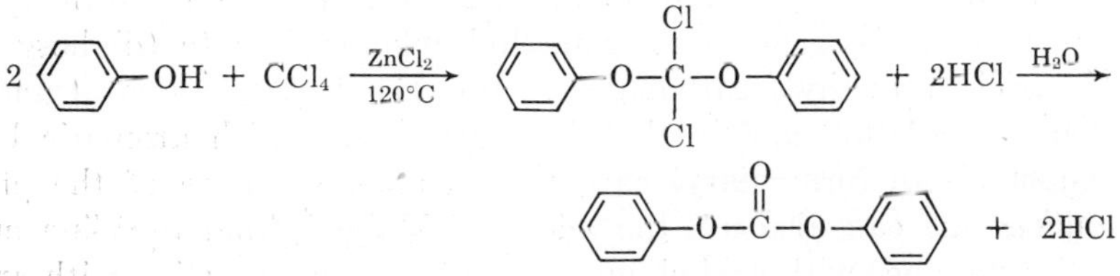

(IV-8)

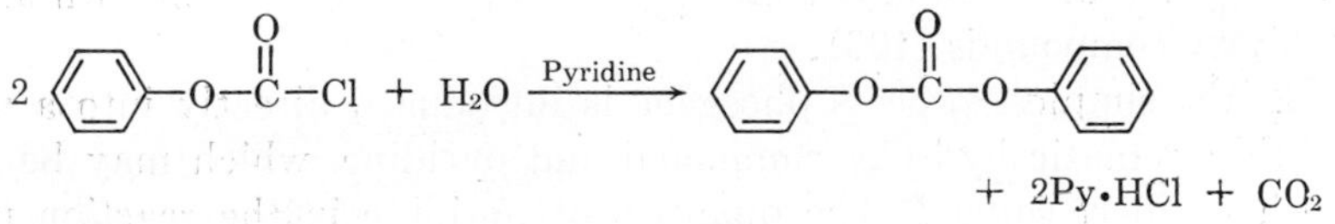

(IV-9)

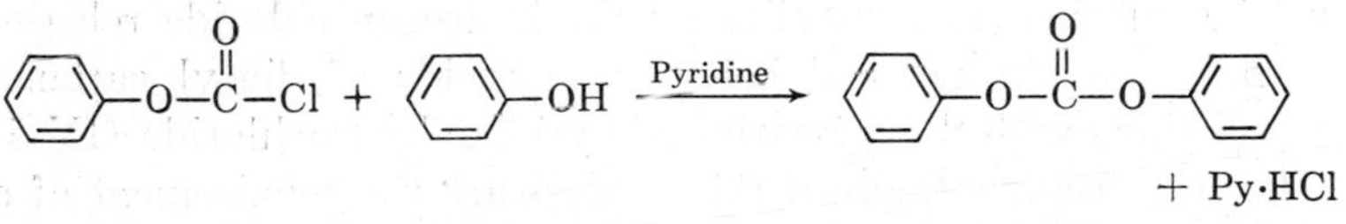

(IV-10)

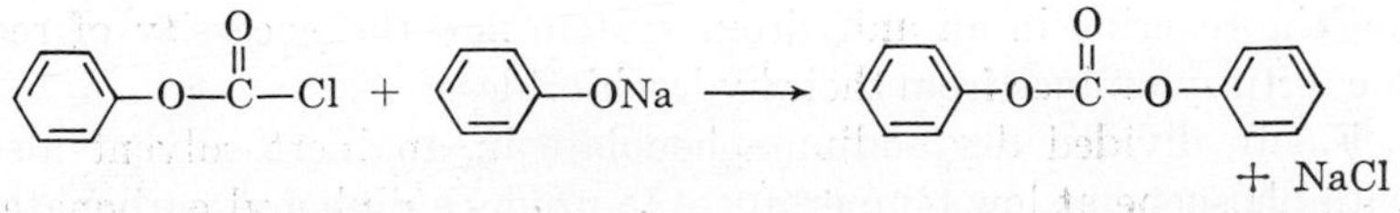

Aromatic hydroxy compounds are much slower to react with phosgene than are hydroxy aliphatics (section III, 1, A, 1). Elevated temperatures are therefore required for the reaction of aromatic hydroxy compounds with phosgene to form chlorocarbonates or diaryl carbonates in accordance with formula IV-4. Satisfactory reaction rates are usually obtained only above 150°C (101).

The more acidic the aromatic hydroxy compounds, the less reactive they are toward phosgene. Halogenated phenols, for example, react slower than phenol. Substitution in the ortho position with regard to the OH-group also decreases the reactivity. In fact, *o,o*-disubstituted phenols usually cannot be made to react with phosgene at all. The direct reaction of phenol with phosgene at 140 to 150°C in a closed system produces diphenyl carbonate in poor yield along with phenyl chlorocarbonate (IV-4) (102). Catalysts of the Friedel-Crafts type, such as $AlCl_3$, accelerate the reaction to the point where at temperature between 180 and 230°C the introduction of phosgene into aromatic hydroxy compounds produces good yields of diaryl carbonates (103).

In the reaction of carbon tetrachloride with phenol in the presence of $ZnCl_2$ and ZnO diphenoxy-dichloromethane is first formed and is then converted into diphenyl carbonate by the water resulting from the neutralization of hydrogen chloride with ZnO (IV-7) (104).

The adducts formed, much like salts, from pyridine or other tertiary amines with phosgene, trichloromethyl chlorocarbonate (diphosgene), or bis-(trichloromethyl) carbonate (section III, 1, A, *1*) react at and below room temperature and in the absence of water with aromatic hydroxy compounds to form diaryl carbonates (105). In place of the phosgene adducts one can also use the adducts obtained from pyridine or other tertiary amines with aryl chlorocarbonates in this reaction with aromatic hydroxy compounds (106).

In the simplest process phosgene is introduced directly into a mixture of the aromatic hydroxy compound and pyridine, which may be diluted with an inert solvent. The quantity of pyridine in the reaction mixture must be sufficient to neutralize all the hydrogen chloride released. Even at room temperatures and below good yields of diaryl carbonates are realized along with the formation of pyridine hydrochloride (IV-5).

The two disadvantages of this process are the requirement of carrying out the reaction in an anhydrous system and the necessity of reclaiming the tertiary amines from their hydrochlorides.

Finely divided dry sodium phenolate in an inert solvent also reacts with phosgene at low temperatures to produce diphenyl carbonate in good yield (IV-6) (107). Diaryl carbonates can also be obtained by introducing phosgene into aqueous solutions of the alkali salts of aromatic hydroxy compounds (108). Some of the phosgene is hydrolyzed in this process, the quantity increasing as the reaction temperature and/or the pH of the solution are raised. In order to attain reasonable yields based on phosgene it is necessary to keep the reaction temperature from rising above 25°C, to dilute the phosgene feed with an inert gas, and to replace the alkali that has been neutralized by phosgene hydrolysis (109).

Phosgene losses are also reduced if aqueous solutions of the alkali salts of aromatic hydroxy compounds are phosgenated at low temperatures in the presence of an inert solvent immiscible with water, e.g., toluene. This is a two-phase reaction requiring constant agitation. From the resulting diphenyl carbonate solutions a refined product is easily isolated by washing the solution, boiling off the solvent, and distilling the diaryl carbonate. Yet, although all these measures tend to cut down phosgene losses, they are still appreciable because comparatively long reaction times are required for high yields. A further decrease of these losses was to be expected if reaction times could be shortened at the low-temperature levels. Bottenbruch and Schnell (110) found, that the reaction of alkali salts of aromatic hydroxy compounds with phosgene to form diaryl carbonates is considerably accelerated by small amounts of tertiary amines or quaternary ammonium bases (section III, 3, A, 2). This effect is even more pronounced if the reaction takes place in a highly dispersed system of the aqueous solution and an immiscible inert solvent capable of dissolving both phosgene and the diaryl carbonate formed (111). In such a process reasonable reaction rates can be attained at and even below 0°C, and at room temperature complete conversion can be realized within a few minutes, which means that the reaction can be carried out continuously without any difficulty. Directions for the continuous preparation of diphenyl carbonate on a laboratory scale follow:

Into a water-cooled 1-liter flask provided with a lateral overflow and agitation, continuously introduce at a temperature of 30°C: 55 g/minute of an aqueous sodium phenolate solution corresponding to 23.55% of phenol and 16.7% of NaOH, 70 g/minute of methylene chloride solution containing 2% of triethylamine, and 7.5 g/minute of phosgene. The reaction mixture is then cascaded through two more water-cooled, agitated overflow vessels sized to give a total reaction time of 14.5 minutes. External cooling holds the temperatures at 30°C in all the vessels. The phases are then separated, the organic phase is washed with water until free of electrolyte, the methylene chloride is boiled off, and the diphenyl carbonate is refined by distillation. b.p.$_9$ = 160°C, m.p. = 79°C. Diphenyl carbonate is obtained at a rate of 13.1

g/minute, representing a yield of 89% based on starting phenol and 100% based on reacted phenol.

The catalytic action of the amine can be explained only by a reaction sequence by which salt-type adducts of phosgene and tertiary amine are formed in the organic phase, which then react at the interface with the alkali salt of the aromatic hydroxy compound to diaryl carbonate, simultaneously liberating the amine and allowing it to return to the organic phase (112). It is surprising in this reaction that the phosgene-amine adducts—easily hydrolyzed as they are by water to CO_2, HCl, and amine—would react at the interface with the alkali salts of the aromatic hydroxy compounds to form diaryl carbonates with such decisive preference that only a very small portion of the phosgene is lost.

Diphenyl carbonate, as are most of the diaryl carbonates, is chemically inert and of high thermal stability when not contaminated. It is easily refined by distillation.

References

1. D. R. Stevens and A. C. Dubbs (to Gulf Research and Development Co.), U. S. Pat. 2,515,906 (1950); A. S. Briggs and J. Haworth (to Imperial Chemical Ind. Ltd.), U. S. Pat. 2,559,932 (1951); D. J. Beaver and R. O. Zerbe (to Monsanto Chemical Co.), U. S. Pats. 2,959,595 (1960), 2,970,151 (1961); A. J. Dietzler

(to The Dow Chemical Co.), U. S. Pats. 2,894,004, 2,917,550 (1959); R. A. Bankert (to Hercules Powder Co.), U. S. Pat. 2,877,210 (1959).

2. G. Bornmann and A. Loeser, *Arzneimittel-Forschg.* (Drug Research), **9,** 9 (1959).

3. J. E. Johnson and D. R. Mussel (to The Dow Chemical Co.), U. S. Pats. 2,535,015 (1950), 2,538,725 (1951).

4. A. Kottler and E. Seeger (to Dr. Karl Thomae G.m.b.H.), U. S. Pat. 2,753,351 (1956).

5. Schw. Pat. 211,116 (1940), Gebr. De Frey A. G.; A. M. Paquin, *Epoxydverbindungen und Epoxydharze,* Springer-Verlag, 1958.

6. H. Schnell and H. Krimm, *Angew. Chem.* **75,** 662 (1963), internat. edit. **2,** 373 (1963).

7. H. Ruppert and H. Schnell (to Farbenfabriken Bayer A. G.), Ger. Pat. 1,135,489 (1963).

8. C. Beck, *Ann.* **194,** 318 (1878).

9. Nölting and Herzberg, *Chemiker Z.* **16,** 185 (1892); N. Caro, *Ber.* **25,** 947 (1892).

10. A. Dianin, *J. russ. physik. chem. Soc.* **1,** 488, 523, 601 (1891); from *Ber.* **25,** Ref. 334 (1892).

11. A. G. Farnham and F. P. Klosek (to Union Carbide Corp.), U. S. Pat. 2,812,364 (1957); J. M. Whelan, Jr. (to Union Carbide Corp.), U. S. Pat. 2,792,429 (1957).

12. H. Pauly and H. Schanz, *Ber.* **56,** 979 (1923).

13. Belg. Pat. 518,457 (1955), Dr. Karl Thomae G.m.b.H.

14. J. Gronowska and B. Szpilewska, *Roczniki Chem.* **34,** 289 (1960).

15. N. J. L. Megson and A. A. Drummond, *J. Soc. Chem. Ind.* (*London*) **49,** 394 (1930); M. Luthy and W. S. Gump (to Burton T. Bush Inc.), U. S. Pat. 2,435,593 (1948); C. L. Moyle and P. A. Wolf (to The Dow Chemical Co.), U. S. Pat. 2,616,932 (1952); F. A. V. Sullivan (to American Cyanamide Co.), U. S. Pats. 2,796,444, 2,796,445 (1957); C. B. Linn (to Universal Oil Products Co.), U. S. Pat. 2,798,079 (1957); O. B. Hager and B. Coe (to Alco Oil and Chemical Corp.), U. S. Pat. 2,932,671 (1960); D. J. Beaver and R. O. Zerbe (to Monsanto Chemical Co.), U. S. Pats. 2,919,294, 2,912,463 (1959); Brit. Pat. 711,122 (1954), N. V. De Bataafsche Petroleum Mij.; F. Andreas, H. Berthold, and W. Heidinger, D. D. R. Pat. 14,472 (1958).

16. A. G. Farnham (to Union Carbide Corp.), Ger. Pat. 1,061,791 (1959).

17. Belg. Pat. 601,797 (1961), Alpine Chemische A. G.

18. F. N. Apel, L. B. Conte, Jr., and H. L. Bender (to Union Carbide Corp.), Fr. Pat. 1,237,656 (1960); F. N. Apel, P. Farevaag, and H. L. Bender (to Union Carbide Corp.), Fr. Pat. 1,244,533 (1960); Belg. Pat. 589,727 (1960), Ciba S. A.

19. E. Korten (to General Aniline Works Inc.), U. S. Pat. 1,760,758 (1930); H. S. Rothrock (to E. I. du Pont de Nemours & Co.), U. S. Pat. 2,069,560 (1937); E. K. Bolton (to E. I. du Pont de Nemours & Co.), U. S. Pat. 2,069,573 (1937).

20. F. V. Morriss, G. F. Bechtle, and T. J. Byerley, *J. Amer. Oil Chemists' Soc.* **37,** 646 (1960).

21. A. Müller, *Chem. Z.* **45,** 632 (1921).

22. S. O. Greenlee (to S. C. Johnson and Son, Inc.), U. S. Pats. 2,907,736, 2,907,737 (1959); A. R. Bader (to S. C. Johnson and Son, Inc.), U. S. Pat. 2,933,520 (1960).

23. D. B. Luten, S. A. Ballard, and C. G. Schwarzer (to Shell Development Co.), U. S. Pat. 2,602,821 (1952).
24. H. Schnell and G. Buchwald (to Farbenfabriken Bayer A. G.), Ger. Pat. 1,075,631 (1960).
25. R. P. Perkins and F. Bryner (to The Dow Chemical Co.), U. S. Pat. 2,359,242 (1944); J. E. Jansen (to B. F. Goodrich Co.), U. S. Pat. 2,468,982 (1949); G. T. Williamson (to Shell Development Co.), U. S. Pats. 2,730,552, 2,730,553, 2,775,620 (1956); J. Scriabine and J. P. M. Bonnart (to Société des Usines Chimiques Rhône-Poulenc), U. S. Pat. 2,923,744 (1960); Fr. Pat. 1,234,620 (1960), Feldmühle, Papier-und Zellstoffwerke A. G.
26. E. J. Reiner, H. S. Schultz, J. G. Shuman, and M. Silberberg (to Technical Tape Corp.), U. S. Pat. 2,762,846 (1956).
27. J. A. Arvin (to E. I. du Pont de Nemours & Co.), U. S. Pat. 1,986,423 (1935).
28. H. L. Bender, F. N. Apel, and L. B. Conte, Jr. (to Union Carbide Corp.), U. S. Pat. 2,936,272 (1960).
29. S. Kohn and E. Schub (to Röhm & Haas Co.), U. S. Pat. 1,978,949 (1934).
30. Brit. Pat. 428,944 (1935), Resinous Products and Chem. Co.
31. H. M. Stanley, J. D. Morgan, and W. L. Pritchard (to The Distillers Co. Ltd.), Brit. Pat. 557,976 (1943).
32. R. P. Perkins (to The Dow Chem. Co.), U. S. Pat. 2,191,831 (1940).
33. R. Greenhalgh (to Imperial Chem. Ind. Ltd.), U. S. Pat. 1,977,627 (1934).
34. J. Schmidlin and R. Lang, *Ber.* **43**, 2806 (1910).
35. Anon., *Petroleum Refiner,* 225 (November 1959).
36. W. F. Christopher and D. W. Fox, *Polycarbonates,* Reinhold, New York, 1962, p. 12.
37. K. H. Meyer and H. Schnell (to Farbenfabriken Bayer A. G.), Ger. Pat. 1,027,205 (1958).
38. H. Ruppert and H. Schnell (to Farbenfabriken Bayer A. G.), Belg. Pat. 602,992 (1961).
39. Fr. Pat. 1,060,888 (1954), N. V. De Bataafsche Petroleum Mij.; P. H. Deming and H. Dannenberg (to Shell Development Co.), U. S. Pat. 2,669,588 (1954); H. Dannenberg (to Shell Development Co.), U. S. Pat. 2,713,072 (1955); M. M. Mosnier and R. V. J. Achard (to Soc. des Usines Chimiques, Rhône-Poulenc), Fr. Pat. 1,037,198 (1953).
40. R. I. Hoaglin, C. W. Plummer, and H. C. Schultze (to Union Carbide Corp.), Brit. Pat. 794,476 (1958); E. C. Britton and F. Bryner (to The Dow Chemical Co.), U. S. Pat. 2,182,308 (1939).
41. G. Fritz and H. Schnell (to Farbenfabriken Bayer A. G.), Belg. Pat. 591,183 (1960).
42. J. P. Abrahams (to Koninklijke Zwavelzuurfabrieken v/h Ketjen N. V.), U. S. Pat. 2,806,068 (1957).
43. H. Heller, L. Bottenbruch, and H. Schnell (to Farbenfabriken Bayer A. G.), Belg. Pat. 611,082 (1961).
44. D. B. Luten, Jr. (to Shell Development Co.), U. S. Pat. 2,791,616 (1957).
45. D. B. Luten, Jr. (to Shell Development Co.), U. S. Pat. 2,845,464 (1958).
46. W. H. Prahl, S. J. Lederman, and E. J. Lichtblau (to Hooker Chem. Corp.), U. S. Pat. 3,073,868 (1963).

47. K. Hultsch, *Chemie der Phenolharze*, Springer-Verlag, 1950.
48. A. H. Filbey and T. H. Coffield (to Ethyl Corp.), U. S. Pat. 2,807,653 (1957); M. S. Kharasch and B. S. Joshi, *J. Org. Chem.* **22**, 1435 (1957).
49. Brit. Pat. 719,101 (1954), Imperial Chemical Ind. Ltd.; R. C. Morris, A. L. Rocklin, and R. E. Vincent (to Shell Intern. Research Mij.), Belg. Pat. 593,606 (1961).
50. H. L. Bender, L. B. Conte, Jr., and F. N. Apel (to Union Carbide Corp.), U. S. Pat. 2,858,342 (1958).
51. H. Krimm, H. Ruppert, and H. Schnell (to Farbenfabriken Bayer A. G.), Belg. Pat. 611,184 (1961).
52. C. G. Schwarzer and D. B. Luten (to Shell Development Co.), U. S. Pat. 2,602,822 (1952).
53. J. P. Henry (to Union Carbide Corp.), U. S. Pat. 2,884,462 (1959).
54. R. I. Hoaglin, C. W. Plummer, and H. C. Schultze (to Union Carbide Corp.), Brit. Pat. 794,476 (1958).
55. J. Furukawa, T. Omae, T. Tsuruta, and S. Nakashio, *Kogyo Kagaku Zasshi* **60**, 803 (1957), from *Chem. Abstracts* **53**, 10, 121f (1959); W. L. Wajsser and W. D. Rjabow, *Doklady Akad. Nauk SSR* **121**, 648 (1958), from *Erdöl und Kohle* **12**, 567 (1959).
56. H. L. Bender, A. G. Farnham, and J. W. Guyer (to Bakelite Corp.), U. S. Pat. 2,464,207 (1949).
57. W. C. Harden and E. E. Reid, *J. Am. Chem. Soc.* **54**, 4325 (1932).
58. N. J. L. Megson and A. A. Drummond, *J. Soc. Chem. Ind. (London)* **49**, 251T (1930).
59. K. Auwers, *Ber.* **40**, 2524 (1907).
60. H. v. Euler, E. Adler, and D. Friedmann, *Arkiv Kemi, Mineral, Geol.* **13B**, No. 12, 1 (1938).
61. K. Auwers, *Ber.* **36**, 1878 (1903).
62. A. Burawoy and J. T. Chamberlain, *J. Chem. Soc. (London)* 624 (1949).
63. H. E. Faith, *J. Am. Chem. Soc.* **72**, 837 (1950).
64. J. C. Ambelang and J. L. Binder, *J. Am. Chem. Soc.* **75**, 947 (1953).
65. A. Deninger, *Ber.* **21**, 1639 (1888).
66. J. v. Braun, *Ann.* **472**, 1 (1929).
67. J. N. Niederl and J. S. McCoy, *J. Am. Chem. Soc.* **63**, 1731 (1941).
68. A. Steiner, *Ber.* **11**, 287 (1878).
69. A. S. Briggs and J. Haworth (to Imperial Chem. Ind. Ltd.), U. S. Pat. 2,559,932 (1951).
70. D. J. Beaver and P. J. Stoffel, *J. Am. Chem. Soc.* **74**, 3410 (1952).
71. H. Schnell, *Angew. Chem.* **68**, 633 (1956).
72. A. Lunjak, *J. russ. physik. chem. Soc.* **36**, 301, from *Chem. Zentr.* 1650, I (1904).
73. A. J. Dietzler and F. Bryner (to The Dow Chem. Co.), U. S. Pat. 2,503,196 (1950).
74. Th. Zinke, *Ann.* **363**, 246 (1908).
75. T. M. Laakso and M. C. Petropoulos (to Kodak S. A.), Belg. Pat. 593,041 (1960).
76. T. M. Laakso, D. A. Buckley, and M. C. Petropoulos (to Kodak S. A.), Belg. Pat. 593,042 (1960).
77. T. M. Laakso and D. A. Buckley (to Kodak S. A.), Belg. Pat. 593,043 (1960).
78. J. E. Driver and J. B. Sousa, *J. Chem. Soc. (London)* 985 (1954).

79. D. J. Beaver and R. O. Zerbe (to Monsanto Chemical Co.), U. S. Pat. 2,912,463 (1959).
80. A. J. Dietzler (to The Dow Chemical Co.), U. S. Pat. 2,917,550 (1959).
81. Brit. Pat. 839,858 (1960), General Electric Co.
82. H. Schnell, *Ind. Eng. Chem.* **51,** 157 (1959).
83. E. Leibnitz and K. Naumann, *Chem. Technik* **3,** 5 (1951).
84. M. E. McGreal, V. Niederl, and J. B. Niederl, *J. Am. Chem. Soc.* **61,** 345 (1939).
85. E. E. Reid and E. Wilson, *J. Am. Chem. Soc.* **66,** 967 (1944).
86. J. C. Sheehan and G. D. Laubach, *J. Am. Chem. Soc.* **72,** 2478 (1950).
87. K. Sisido, H. Nozaki, and T. Iwako, *J. Am. Chem. Soc.* **71,** 2037 (1949).
88. K. Sisido, H. Nozaki, and O. Kurihara, *J. Am. Chem. Soc.* **72,** 2270 (1950).
89. L. H. Baekeland and H. L. Bender, *Ind. Eng. Chem.* **17,** 225 (1925).
90. J. B. Niederl and R. H. Nagel, *J. Am. Chem. Soc.* **63,** 1235 (1941).
91. R. P. Perkins and F. Bryner (to The Dow Chem. Co.), Ger. Pat. 905,977 (1954).
92. A. R. Bader and A. D. Kontowicz, *J. Am. Chem. Soc.* **76,** 4465 (1954).
93. S. O. Greenlee (to S. C. Johnson and Son, Inc.), Ger. Pat. Appl. 1,110,629 (1961).
94. R. A. Mathes (to B. F. Goodrich Co.), U. S. Pat. 2,883,365 (1959).
95. C. Haeussermann and E. Bauer, *Ber.* **30,** 738 (1897).
96. G. Tassinari, *Gazz. Chim. Ital.* **17,** 83 (1887).
97. S. Smiles and A. W. Bain, *J. Chem. Soc. (London)* **91,** 1119 (1907).
98. J. Annahaim, *Ann.* **172,** 28 (1874).
99. E. M. Richardson and E. E. Reid, *J. Am. Chem. Soc.* **62,** 413 (1940).
100. Brit. Pat. 835,465 (1960), General Electric Co.
101. S. Petersen, H. F. Piepenbrink, A. Mitrowsky, H. Dorlars, in E. Müller, ed., *Methoden der organ. Chemie (Houben-Weyl)*, Georg Thieme-Verlag, Stuttgart, Vol. VIII/III, 1952, pp. 101ff.
102. Th. Kempf. *J. Prakt. Chem. [2]* **1,** 402 (1870).
103. S. Tryon and W. S. Benedict (to General Chem. Co.), U. S. Pat. 2,362,865 (1944).
104. M. Gomberg and H. R. Snow, *J. Am. Chem. Soc.* **47,** 198 (1925).
105. Ger. Pats. 109,933 (1898); 116,386 (1899); 117,346 (1898); Chemische Fabrik von Heyden A. G.
106. Ger. Pat. 118,566 (1899), Farbenfabriken vorm. Friedrich Bayer u. Comp.; Ger. Pat. 116,386 (1899), Chemische Fabrik von Heyden A. G.
107. C. A. Bischoff and A. v. Hedenstroem, *Ber.* **35,** 3431 (1902).
108. W. Hentschel, *J. Prakt. Chem. [2]* **27,** 39 (1883); *Ber.* **17,** 1284 (1884); Ger. Pat. 24,151 (1883), Chem. Fabrik vorm. Hofmann u. Schoetensack.
109. J. H. Pearson and S. Tryon (to General Chem. Co.), U. S. Pat. 2,335,441 (1943).
110. L. Bottenbruch and H. Schnell (to Farbenfabriken Bayer A. G.), Ger. Pat. 1,101,386 (1961).
111. K. H. Meyer and H. Schnell (to Farbenfabriken Bayer A. G.), Ger. Pat. 1,056,141 (1959).
112. H. Schnell. *Angew. Chem.* **73,** 629 (1961).

V. STRUCTURE AND PROPERTIES OF AROMATIC POLYCARBONATES

Little is known about the internal structure of or the properties possessed by the aliphatic and aliphatic-aromatic polycarbonates. What information on this subject has been published to date is covered in sections III, 1, B and III, 2 of this book.

As processes were developed for the commercial production of polycarbonates based on bisphenol A and areas of application opened up for this new plastic, many laboratories turned to research concerning the behavior and constitution of this polymer. Although these investigations have contributed much to the understanding of the, in so many respects, unusual properties of the aromatic polycarbonates, there still has not emerged a clear pattern correlating the physical properties, the chemical nature, and the morphological characteristics of this thermoplastic material. This chapter is devoted to a discussion of the studies made to date.

So far, only the bisphenol A based polycarbonates have been at all thoroughly investigated. What work has been reported dealing with the properties of polycarbonates derived from other dihydroxy compounds or those of aromatic polycarbonate copolymers has been of an exploratory nature only.

1. SOLUBILITY OF AROMATIC POLYCARBONATES (1–5)

The solubility of aromatic polycarbonates is dependent primarily upon their crystalline state and the nature of the aromatic dihydroxy compounds used in their preparation. Polycarbonates which crystallize both quickly and extensively, e.g., the polycarbonates obtained from hydroquinone, 4,4'-dihydroxy-diphenyl methane, and 4,4'-dihydroxy-diphenyl-1,2-ethane, are not soluble in any of the conventional solvents.

Table V-1 shows that polycarbonates based on 4,4'-dihydroxy-diphenyl alkanes in a state of inhibited crystallinity, as realized by rapid cooling from the liquid state or by rapid evaporation of the solvent from a solution, are soluble in several of the commonly employed solvents, such as methylene chloride, m-cresol, pyridine, and dimethyl formamide. In many other solvents they swell.

TABLE V-1

Solubility of Aromatic Polycarbonates

Polycarbonate made from	Methylene chloride	m-Cresol	Ethyl acetate	Acetone	Cyclo-hexanone	Tetra-hydro-furane	Benzene	Pyridine	Di-methyl-form-amide
4,4'-Dihydroxy-diphenyl methane	0	0	-	-	-	-	-	0	0
" -diphenyl-1,2-ethane	-	-	-	-	-	-	-	-	-
" -diphenyl-1,1-ethane	+	+	0	0	+	+	+	+	+
" -diphenyl-1,1-isobutane	+	+	+	0	+	+	0	+	+
" -diphenyl-2,2-propane	+	+	0	0	+	0	0	+	+
" -diphenyl-4,4-heptane	+	+	+	0	0	+	+	+	+
" -diphenyl-2,2-hexane	+	+	+	0	0	+	+	+	+
" -triphenyl-2,2,2-ethane	+	+	0	0	+	+	+	+	+
" -diphenyl-1,1-cyclo-hexane	+	+	0	0	+	+	+	+	+
" -diphenyl-β,β-decahydronaphthalene	+	+	0	0	+	+	+	+	+
" -3,3'-dimethyl-diphenyl-2,2-propane	+	+	+	0	+	+	+	+	+
" -3,3',5,5'-tetra-chloro-diphenyl-2,2-propane	-	-	+	0	+	+	+	+	+
" -diphenyl sulfone	+	+	-	-	+	+	-	+	+
" -diphenyl sulfoxide	+	+	-	-	+	0	-	+	+
" -diphenyl sulfide	-	+	-	-	+	0	-	+	+
" -diphenyl ether	-	+	-	-	+	0	-	+	+

+ = soluble, 0 = swells, - = insoluble.

Substituents attached to the central carbon atom of the 4,4′-dihydroxy-diphenyl methane derivatives and/or to the aromatic residues generally increase the solubility. Polycarbonate copolymers are also more soluble than the corresponding homopolymers.

A number of aromatic polycarbonates and copolycarbonates, e.g., the polycarbonate made from 4,4′-dihydroxy-diphenyl-1,1-cyclohexane and its copolymers with bisphenol A, are soluble in solvents suitable for coatings such as esters, ketones, cyclic ethers, and aromatic hydrocarbons. Solutions of crystallizable polycarbonates with high solid content will gel by crystallization.

For those aromatic polycarbonates that have the capacity to crystallize the solubility or swelling tendency is greatly reduced by a high degree of crystallization or a combination of molecular orientation and crystallinity. None of the aromatic polycarbonates examined so far is soluble in water, aliphatic hydroxy compounds, carboxylic acids, or aliphatic and cyclo-aliphatic hydrocarbons.

The following were found to be practical solvents for polycarbonate made from bisphenol A: 1,1,2,2-tetrachloroethane, methylene chloride, cis-1,2-dichloroethylene, chloroform, and 1,1,2-trichloroethane.

Compounds having only a very limited dissolving capacity are 1,2-di-chloroethane, thiophene, dioxane, tetrahydrofurane, acetophenone, ani-sole, benzonitrile, cyclohexanone, dimethyl formamide, and nitrobenzene.

Swelling effects are observed with benzene, chlorobenzene, 1,2-dichlo-robenzene, 1-chloronaphthalene, tetrahydronaphthalene, diphenyl ether, epichlorohydrine, glycol carbonate, acetone, ethyl acetate, carbon tetra-chloride, nitromethane, acetonitrile, and 1,1-dichloroethane.

Aliphatic and cycloaliphatic hydrocarbons, ethers, and carboxylic acids neither dissolve nor swell this family of polycarbonates (5).

On one hand the solubility of many aromatic polycarbonates in fre-quently used solvents, particularly methylene chloride, facilitates proc-essing into coatings, films, and fibers by solvent evaporation, using meth-ods and equipment considered standard in the plastics industry. On the other hand, the fact that they will dissolve or swell in the presence of many organic solvents naturally limits their application.

2. MELTING RANGE AND SECOND-ORDER TRANSITION TEMPERATURES OF AROMATIC POLYCARBONATES (1–4)

At a low degree of crystallization the aromatic polycarbonates with inhibited crystallinity have no well-defined melting point. Somewhere above the second-order transition temperature they begin to soften and their transition from the liquid to the solid state takes place over a range of temperature which often covers a span of 10 to 20°C. Since the melt viscosity of high molecular weight aromatic polycarbonates is extremely high in the vicinity of the melting point (section V, 4), it is quite difficult to pinpoint the exact moment of transition from solid to liquid by any one of the conventional methods for melting-point determination.

For high crystallized aromatic polycarbonates having a crystal size larger than the wavelength of visible light an optical melting point can be defined as the temperature at which all double refraction disappears; this phenomenon is found to occur at a temperature substantially above the melting range of less crystalline, optically clear samples of the same material. For example, polycarbonate made from bisphenol A as it is obtained by rapid cooling from the molten state or by quick evaporation of the solvent from a solution in methylene chloride has a melting range of 220 to 230°C, whereas the same polymer in a highly crystalline state does not lose its refractive properties until heated as high as 255 to 265°C. A similar behavior is observed for the polycarbonate based on 4,4'-di-hydroxy-diphenyl methane, which at a low degree of crystallization will

TABLE V-2

Melting Ranges and Second-Order Transition Temperatures of Polycarbonates Based on 4,4'-Dihydroxy-Diphenyl Methane Derivatives Carrying One Substituent Attached to the Central Carbon Atom

Polycarbonate made from HO—⟨ ⟩—C(H)(R)—⟨ ⟩—OH wherein R =	Melting range [°C]	Second-order transition temperature [°C]
—H	223–225	147
—CH$_3$	185–195	130
—CH$_2$—CH$_2$—CH$_3$	150–170	123
—CH(CH$_3$)(CH$_3$)	170–180	149
—⟨ ⟩ (phenyl)	200–215	121

melt between 223 and 225°C while remaining a solid to much higher temperatures if highly crystallized.

The melting ranges of aromatic polycarbonates and copolycarbonates compiled in Tables III-6 and III-7 and discussed in the following pages of this chapter should, incidentally, be considered approximate data only because in many cases neither the crystalline state of the samples nor the method used for the melting-point determination was reported.

Much more reliable are the data for the second-order transition point, since the temperature can be determined by physical methods, such as refractometric or dilatometric measurements at different temperatures, which are quite exact as well as being easily reproducible (6). In an attempt to gain a better understanding of the particular properties of the aromatic polycarbonates based on 4,4′-dihydroxy-diphenyl alkanes, it is quite interesting to relate melting characteristics of the different polycarbonates to the nature of the aromatic dihydroxy compounds used in building up the polymer (Table V-2).

TABLE V-3

Melting Ranges and Second-Order Transition Temperatures of Polycarbonates Based on 4,4′-Dihydroxy-Diphenyl Methane Derivatives Carrying One —CH_3 and One Other Substituent Attached to the Central Carbon Atom

Polycarbonate made from $$HO-\!\!\left\langle\bigcirc\right\rangle\!\!-\!\!\underset{\underset{R}{|}}{\overset{\overset{CH_3}{|}}{C}}\!\!-\!\!\left\langle\bigcirc\right\rangle\!\!-OH$$ wherein R =	Melting range [°C]	Second-order transition temperature [°C]
—CH_3	220–230	149
—CH_2—CH_3	205–222	134
—CH_2—CH_2—CH_3	200–220	137
—CH_2—$(CH_2)_2$—CH_3	180–200	
—CH_2—$(CH_2)_5$—CH_3	170–190	
$$-CH_2-CH\!\!\underset{\diagdown CH_3}{\overset{\diagup CH_3}{}}$$	200–220	
$-\!\!\left\langle\bigcirc\right\rangle$	210–230	176

In the series of polymers shown in Table V-2 an increase in size of the substituent R from H to methyl to propyl brings about a decrease of the melting and second-order transition temperatures, since the asymmetrical structure causes a separation of the molecular chains, a phenomenon which is also observed in other crystallizable thermoplastic polymers. However, the introduction of more bulky or voluminous substituents, such as the isopropyl or phenyl residues, does not cause a further decrease in the melting and second-order transition temperatures; in fact, these temperatures are raised again.

The polycarbonates listed in Table V-3 again show the influence of an asymmetrically substituted 4,4'-dihydroxy-diphenyl methane derivative

TABLE V-4

Melting Ranges and Second-Order Transition Temperatures of Polycarbonates Based on 4,4'-Dihydroxy-Diphenyl Methane Derivatives with a Symmetrically Substituted Central Carbon Atom and Those in which the Central Carbon Atom Constitutes Part of a Cycloaliphatic Ring

Polycarbonate made from 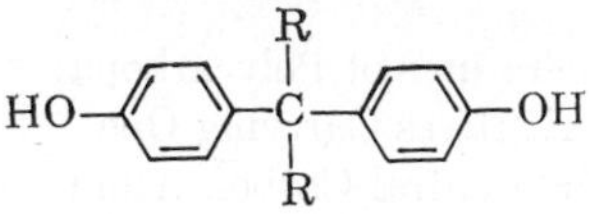 $HO-\!\!\langle\bigcirc\rangle\!\!-\overset{\overset{R}{\mid}}{\underset{\underset{R}{\mid}}{C}}-\!\!\langle\bigcirc\rangle\!\!-OH$ wherein R =	Melting range [°C]	Second-order transition temperature [°C]
—H	223–225	147
—CH₃	220–230	149
—CH₂—CH₂—CH₃	190–200	148
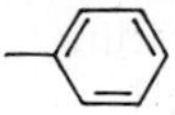 $\langle\bigcirc\rangle$	210–230	121

Polycarbonate made from

$HO-\!\!\langle\bigcirc\rangle\!\!-R-\!\!\langle\bigcirc\rangle\!\!-OH$

wherein R =		
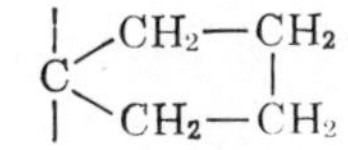 $\overset{\mid}{\underset{\mid}{C}}\!\!\begin{array}{c}{}_{CH_2-CH_2}\\{}_{CH_2-CH_2}\end{array}$	240–250	167
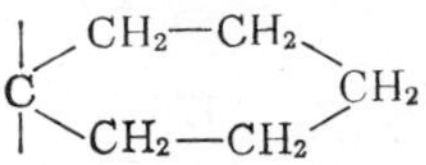 $\overset{\mid}{\underset{\mid}{C}}\!\!\begin{array}{c}{}^{CH_2-CH_2}\\{}_{CH_2-CH_2}\end{array}\!\!CH_2$	250–260	171

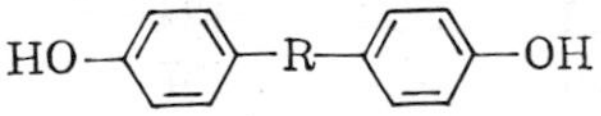

on the melting behavior. The effect, however, is not very pronounced. Increasing the length of the alkyl residues from 1 to 7 carbon atoms brings the melting range down only about 50°C. Bulky substituents, such as an isopropyl or phenyl residues, again bring about comparatively high melting and second-order transition temperatures.

The same kind of data for polycarbonates based on 4,4'-dihydroxy-diphenyl methane derivatives with a symmetrically substituted central carbon atom and those in which the central carbon atom forms part of a cycloaliphatic ring are compiled in Table V-4.

Symmetrical substitution of the central carbon atom in a 4,4'-dihydroxy-diphenyl methane derivative with alkyl or aryl residues appears to have little effect upon the melting temperature or second-order transition temperatures of the corresponding polycarbonate. When the central carbon atom of this base molecule constitutes part of a cycloaliphatic ring, comparatively high values for these temperature stability limits are obtained.

Table V-5 is intended to show the changes in melting range and second-order transition temperature of polycarbonates which are caused by substituents attached to the aromatic rings of the basic 4,4'-dihydroxy-diphenyl methane derivatives.

Symmetric substitution with halogens in the 3,3',5,5'-positions of 4,4'-dihydroxy-diphenyl methane causes higher melting ranges and second-order transition temperatures in the corresponding polycarbonates. 4,4'-Dihydroxy-diphenyl methane derivatives similarly substituted with alkyl or aryl residues have not yet been converted to polycarbonates because they are difficult if not impossible to react with carbonic acid derivatives.

In cases in which both phenyl residues are substituted by a halogen atom or an alkyl group in one of the o-positions to the hydroxyl groups a distinct reduction of melting and second-order transition temperatures of the resulting polycarbonate is noted, although this decrease is only slight if the substitution is confined to one of the phenyls.

It should be emphasized at this point that the data compiled in the foregoing tables show all the polycarbonates based on 4,4'-dihydroxy-diphenyl methane derivatives, which have so far been investigated, to melt somewhere between 150 and 260°C, a temperature range considered advantageous for commercial thermoplastic applications, whereas all their second-order transition temperatures, varying between 120 and 180°C, are extremely high by comparison with other thermoplastics.

TABLE V-5

Effect of Substitutions to the Phenol Residues of 4,4′-Dihydroxy-Diphenyl Methane Derivatives upon Melting Range and Second-Order Transition Temperature of the Resulting Polycarbonates

Polycarbonate made from	Melting range [°C]	Second-order transition temperature [°C]
$HO-C_6H_4-CH_2-C_6H_4-OH$	223–225	147
$HO-C_6H_2(Cl)_2-CH_2-C_6H_2(Cl)_2-OH$	234–239	...
$HO-C_6H_4-C(C_4H_8)-C_6H_4-OH$ (cyclopentylidene)	250–260	171
$HO-C_6H_2(Cl)_2-C(C_4H_8)-C_6H_2(Cl)_2-OH$ (cyclopentylidene)	260–270	163
$HO-C_6H_4-C(CH_3)_2-C_6H_4-OH$	220–230	149
$HO-C_6H_2(Cl)_2-C(CH_3)_2-C_6H_2(Cl)_2-OH$	250–260	180

(TABLE V-5) *continued*

Polycarbonate made from	Melting range [°C]	Second-order transition temperature [°C]
	240–260	157
	190–210	147
	150–170	95
	210–220	140
	215–222	145
	200–220	112
	192–195	132

Bulky or voluminous substituents attached to the central carbon atom of 4,4'-dihydroxy-diphenyl methane derivatives have the peculiar effect of not lowering but, on the contrary, of considerably raising the melting and second-order transition temperatures of the corresponding poly-carbonates. An increase in these temperatures is also caused by sym-metrical halogen substitutions of both phenyl residues in both o,o'-posi-tions to the hydroxyl groups, whereas halogen atoms, alkyl-, alkoxyl-, or cycloalkyl residues substituted in only one o-position to the hydroxyl groups of either one or both phenyl residues cause them to be reduced. Although at first glance such behavior seems contradictory, it can be made plausible if the interaction of several independent causes is assumed.

First, the carbonic acid ester group appears to contribute very little to the intermolecular forces. This follows from the comparatively low melt-ing point of the aliphatic polycarbonates (section III, 1, B) as well as from the fact that for comparable aromatic polycarbonates the weight ratio of the

$$-O-\overset{\overset{\textstyle O}{\|}}{C}-O-\text{-groups}$$

to the molecule as a whole appears to have but a negligible effect. Thus it can be seen in Table V-6 that reduc-ing the weight per cent of

$$-O-\overset{\overset{\textstyle O}{\|}}{C}-O-$$

in the total polymer from 23.6 to 16.1% in comparably constructed macromolecules raises the melting range and second-order transition temperature.

Somewhat stronger is the influence of the side valences acting between the aromatic residues. This can be deduced from Table V-5, which shows the influence on the polycarbonate melting behavior of substituents at-taching to the aromatic residues in the 4,4'-dihydroxy-diphenyl methane derivatives.

Finally, a strong effect on the thermal properties must be attributed to factors determining the degree of mobility of the macromolecule within the solid substance. Otherwise one could not understand the significant increases in the melting and second-order transition temperatures of poly-carbonates, where the central atom of the 4,4'-dihydroxy-diphenyl meth-ane derivative carries a bulky or voluminous substituent. Such substit-uents apparently restrain the rotation of the phenyl residues with regard to the central carbon atom and thereby cause a further stiffening of the macromolecule which adds to its inherent rigidity resulting from the close approximation of aromatic rings.

TABLE V-6

Melting Range and Second-Order Transition Temperature of Comparable Aromatic Polycarbonates as a Function of the Weight Ratio of the —O—C(=O)—O— Groups to the Total Molecular Weight

Polycarbonate	Melting range [°C]	Second-order transition temperature [°C]	Weight ratio of the —O—C(=O)—O— groups to total molecular weight [%]
$H-\left[O-\left\langle\text{C}_6\text{H}_4\right\rangle-\underset{\underset{CH_3}{\overset{CH_3}{|}}}{C}-\left\langle\text{C}_6\text{H}_4\right\rangle-O-\overset{O}{\underset{}{C}}\right]_x$	220–230	149	23.6
$H-\left[O-\left\langle\text{C}_6\text{H}_4\right\rangle-\underset{\underset{CH_3}{\overset{CH_3}{|}}}{C}-\left\langle\text{C}_6\text{H}_4\right\rangle-\underset{\underset{CH_3}{\overset{CH_3}{|}}}{C}-\left\langle\text{C}_6\text{H}_4\right\rangle-O-\overset{O}{\underset{}{C}}\right]_x$	230–250	162	16.1

3. DETERMINATION OF THE MOLECULAR DATA OF POLYCARBONATES IN SOLUTION

All experimental work reported to date dealing with the determination of molecular data in solution has been carried out on polycarbonates produced by various methods from bisphenol A. Since this polymer is completely soluble in suitable solvents, such as methylene chloride, tetrahydrofuran, chloroform, and dioxane, it can be separated into molecular weight fractions and is subject to investigation by the standard solution viscosity, osmotic pressure, ultracentrifuging, diffusion, light scattering, and turbidimetric titration techniques. The following pages are devoted to a description of how these methods have been applied to bisphenol A polycarbonate and the results that have been obtained. The symbols, definitions, and units, as well as the general nomenclature used throughout this section, are in accordance with the *Richtlinien für die Nomenklatur auf dem Gebiet der makromolekularen Stoffe* (7).

For many lines of inquiry it is important to be able to analyze not only the polymolecular material as is but also fractions of the narrowest possible molecular weight range. The fractionation techniques developed for polycarbonates therefore occupy a central position.

A. Fractionation of Bisphenol A Polycarbonate

The first fractionations of bisphenol A polycarbonates produced by the phosgenation (section III, 3, A, 2) and ester exchange (section III, 3, A, 4) processes were carried out by successive precipitation, using methylene chloride as the solvent and methanol as the precipitant at 28°C (1). Since the liquid phases of this system are easily separated, a fairly good fractionating effect is realized.

There is a disadvantage to the use of this system, however, in that a certain amount of degradation is sometimes observed. This is probably due to alcoholysis of the macromolecule under the catalytic influence of trace impurities, particularly alkalies.

Also the possibility of hydrolysis cannot be altogether discounted, since it is extremely difficult to have an absolutely anhydrous methylene chloride-methanol system. The methylene chloride-petroleum fraction (boiling point 30–50°C) system was therefore used by Schulz and Horbach (8). Under suitable conditions this system will yield two liquid phases and allow a fractionating effect to be obtained without degradation. Methylene chloride solutions containing petroleum fraction, however, have a tendency to precipitate the polymer in crystalline form.

Since it is impossible as a rule to redissolve these crystalline solids by raising the temperature, such solids must be avoided, which means carrying out the fractionation in a large number of steps by adding the precipitant in very small quantities.

The amount of precipitant added in any one step should never be sufficient to cause visible turbidity. Considerable time is required for the separation of the liquid phases. The successive fractionation by this method of a bisphenol A polycarbonate with a weight average molecular weight $\bar{M}_w$ of 36,000 would be carried out in the following manner:

At 25°C 7.2 l of a petroleum fraction of a boiling point of 30–50°C is added to 8 l of a methylene chloride solution containing 2.5 g/l of polycarbonate, and the mixture is allowed to settle at this temperature for 24 hours. The heavy phase which by then will have settled is separated and the solvent is evaporated from this phase at atmospheric pressure and 65°C. Subsequent drying at 65°C, first under moderate and then under high vacuum, will yield a first fraction of less than 0.1 g of polycarbonate. Fractionation of the supernatant phase is continued in the same manner by adding 100–150 ml of the above petroleum fraction at a time, which will yield fractions between 0.2 and 2.0 g of polycarbonate in 20 or more successive steps.

The abovementioned difficulties prohibit the addition of larger portions of precipitant to obtain larger fractions.

Figure V-1 shows a plot of the integral distribution curve obtained by this method.

The triangle fractionation technique reported by Meyerhoff (9) requires more effort but is also more effective. For the same polycarbonate it yields in the same solvent-nonsolvent system the integral distribution shown in Figure V-1 (8).

Fractionation by successive precipitation, and even more so by the triangle method, is tedious and time-consuming, which renders these techniques of little practical value for routine analytical work.

A considerably quicker and less involved technique is the fractional extraction method introduced by Fuchs (10). With this method the analysis of a sample identical to those used in the successive precipitation and triangle fractionations above would be carried out as follows:

Six squares or rectangles cut from 18 μ aluminum foil, having a combined surface area of 1600 cm^2, are dipped into a methylene chloride solution of the polycarbonate, which contains 40 g/l of solids. As the

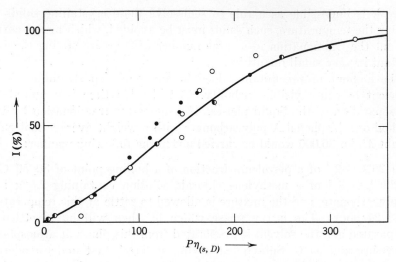

Fig. V-1. Integral distribution curves of a bisphenol A polycarbonate, $M\eta_{(s,D)} = 36{,}000$, obtained by successive precipitation O, triangle fractionation ◑, and fractional extraction ●.

coupons are withdrawn from the solution, excess liquid will drip off and of the remainder the bulk of the solvent will evaporate rapidly to the atmosphere. Drying for 2 hours at 65°C under medium high vacuum is then done. If the method is to be used for fractionating a higher molecular weight polycarbonate, the concentration of the dipping solution is appropriately reduced. Should the thickness of the polycarbonate coating be somewhat greater near the edges of the coupons, they can be trimmed before being cut into strips approximately 1 cm wide. These strips are then placed into the 300-ml double-wall extraction vessel, described by Fuchs (10). To obtain the first fraction, the vessel is filled with a mixture of 48 volume per cent of methylene chloride and 52 volume per cent of petroleum fraction (b.p. 30–50°C) and shaken for 10 minutes at 25°C. The resulting solution is removed from the vessel, the solvent and nonsolvent evaporated, and the remaining solids, constituting the first fraction, are dried at 65°C under medium high vacuum to zero weight loss (48 hours). In the same manner the coated coupons are extracted with a succession of solvent precipitant mixtures with progressively increasing solvent power to obtain the other fractions. Pure solvent is used in the last step.

The weights of the fractions obtained are shown in Table V-7 opposite the solvent composition used in each extraction step.

Similar results are obtained, if a methylene chloride-cyclohexane solvent system is used for fractional extraction (11).

The three foregoing fractionation methods are compared with regard to their effectiveness in Figure V-1. This graph combines the results of three fractionations of a bisphenol A polycarbonate having a molecular weight of $M_{\eta(s,D)} = 36,000$ carried out by successive precipitation, tri-

TABLE V-7

Solvent Compositions and Weight Fractions Obtained by Fractional Extraction of a Bisphenol A Polycarbonate [$M_{\eta(s,D)} = 36,000$]

| | Solvent | | |
Fraction No.	Methylene chloride [vol %]	Petroleum fraction [vol %]	Weight of fraction [g]
1	48.0	52.0	0.1487
2	48.5	51.5	0.0651
3	49.0	51.0	0.0486
4	49.5	50.5	0.0364
5	50.0	50.0	0.0281
6	50.5	49.5	0.0271
7	51.0	49.0	0.0256
8	54.0	46.0	0.0722
9	100	. . .	0.0976

angle fractionation, and fractional extraction, respectively. The curves show integral per cent versus degree of polymerization. The term integral per cent (I%) is defined as the combined weight percentage of all molecules with a degree of polymerization from zero up to and including P. The degree of polymerization of each fraction was calculated from solution viscosity measurements calibrated by sedimentation, diffusion, and light-scattering data (section V, 3, B, C, E).

The best fractionation effect is obtained by the triangle fractionation method (solid curve in Fig. V-1). Successive precipitation and fractional extraction are less effective.

Fractionation data reported by Schulz (12) were used to calculate heterogeneity index (13) for commercial bisphenol A polycarbonates. These were found to vary from 0.3 to 0.6, showing that the uniformity of these polymers is greater than that of a normal distribution curve.

Physical separation of the fractions is avoided in the turbidimetric titration method described by Morey and Tamblyn (14) for determining the mass distribution curve.

Kroser, Veinrieb, and Silina (15) used a Pulfrich nephelometer to measure the light scattered by a very dilute $(2.5 \times 10^{-5} \text{ g/ml})$ bisphenol A polycarbonate solution in chloroform at 18°C, following the stepwise addition of methanol as a precipitant; equilibrium was established between steps. The size of the precipitated particles was shown to be independent of the molecular weight. The measured turbidities as a function of the amount of precipitant added were used to calculate the distribution function in accordance with the Morey and Tamblyn (14) method. The interpretation of the data was based on calibrations with fractions of known molecular weight obtained by successive precipitation of a bisphenol A polycarbonate from a chloroform solution with petroleum fraction ($M = 16,000 - 213,000$). The resulting distribution curves show turbidimetric titration to be an easy-to-use method for determining characteristic differences in the molecular weight distribution of polycarbonates, thus at least making it suitable for production control.

B. Diffusion and Sedimentation Measurements on Bisphenol A Polycarbonate Solutions

Data from diffusion and sedimentation measurements on dilute polycarbonate solutions can be used to calculate the molecular weight as well as the second osmotic virial coefficient. Schulz and Horbach (8) carried out sedimentation studies on bisphenol A polycarbonate solutions with the ultracentrifuge, using a field of 1.7×10^5 g at 20°C. Tetrahydrofuran was selected as the solvent. Methylene chloride is not suitable because of its higher specific gravity as compared to polycarbonate.

The diffusion of polycarbonates from dilute solutions into pure solvent at 20°C was also measured by Schulz and Horbach (8), using a Meyerhoff (16) sliding cell and methylene chloride as well as tetrahydrofuran as solvents.

The sedimentation and diffusion constants extrapolated to infinite dilution (s_0 and D_0) are used to calculate the molecular weight according to Svedberg as

(V-1)
$$M_{s,D} = \frac{s_0 R T}{D_0 (1 - V_2 \cdot \rho_1)}$$

wherein V_2 is the partial specific volume, in this case equal to the apparent specific volume, of the polymer and ρ_1 is the density of the solvent. For bisphenol A polycarbonates in tetrahydrofuran solution at 20°C the diffusion constant extrapolated to infinite dilution (D_0) is related to the molecular weight $M_{s,D}$ by the correlation

$$(V\text{-}2) \qquad\qquad \frac{1}{D_0} = 1.57 \times 10^3 \times M_{s,D}^{0.64}$$

For methylene chloride solutions at 20°C the relationship is

$$(V\text{-}3) \qquad\qquad \frac{1}{D_0} = 4.89 \times 10^2 \times M_{s,D}^{0.73}$$

Similarly, the sedimentation constant extrapolated to infinite dilution s_0 measured in tetrahydrofuran solution at 20°C is related to the molecular weight $M_{s,D}$ by the correlation

$$(V\text{-}4) \qquad\qquad s_0 = 1.33 \times 10^{-14} \times M_{s,D}^{0.36}$$

Equations V-2, V-3, and V-4 make it possible to calculate the molecular weight $M_{s,D}$ of bisphenol A polycarbonates directly from measurements of the sedimentation and diffusion constants in dilute solution as functions of the solution concentration at 20°C, using tetrahydrofuran, in the case of diffusion measurements, tetrahydrofuran, or methylene chloride as the solvent.

According to Schulz and Meyerhoff (17), the second virial coefficient $\overline{B}$ of the osmotic equation can be calculated from the slopes of the diffusion constant and the reciprocal of the sedimentation constant plotted against concentration to

$$(V\text{-}5) \qquad\qquad \overline{B} = \frac{RT}{2M} (K_s + K_D)$$

whereby K_s and K_D are the concentration gradients of the diffusion constant and the reciprocal sedimentation constant, respectively.

C. Light-Scattering Measurements on Bisphenol A Polycarbonate Solutions

Measurements of the intensity of light scattered by dilute solutions of macromolecular substances can be used to determine molecular weight, molecule dimensions, and the second osmotic virial coefficient. Bisphenol A polycarbonate solutions, both in methylene chloride (8,11) and in chloroform (18), have been investigated by light-scattering techniques. The methylene chloride and chloroform solutions are first filtered through fritted glass. When doing this a change in concentration must be considered, for the fritted glass will absorb measurable quantities of polycarbonate. Dioxane solutions may also be clarified by centrifuging.

When using a vertically polarized incident beam, the molecular weight may be calculated by the Debye equation

$$(V-6) \qquad \frac{Kc}{R_\theta} = \frac{1}{\bar{M}_w P_\theta} + 2\bar{B}c$$

where P_θ is the scattering factor $(R_\theta/R_0)_{c \to 0}$ used to correct for intramolecular interference and $\bar{B}$ is the second osmotic virial coefficient. The constant K is calculated from the refractive index n_0 of the solvent, the wavelength λ_0 of the polarized incident beam (in vacuum), and the change of the solution refractive index with concentration $\partial n/\partial c$ as

$$(V-7) \qquad K = \frac{4\pi^2 n_0^2}{N_A \lambda_0^4} \cdot \left(\frac{\partial n}{\partial c}\right)^2$$

The increments of the refractive index for a number of bisphenol A polycarbonate solutions are summarized in Table V-8 as related to temperature and wavelength.

TABLE V-8

Increments of the Refractive Index of Bisphenol A Polycarbonate Solutions for Various Temperatures and Wavelengths

Temperature [°C]	Wavelength [Å]	$\partial n/\partial c$		
		Methylene chloride (8)	Tetrahydro-furan (8)	Chloro-form (18)
7	5740	0.1538	0.1753	. . .
7	5530	0.1547	0.1765	. . .
7	4350	0.1660	0.1889	. . .
20	5461	0.1589	. . .	
20	4358	0.1631	. . .	0.165
25	4358	0.1760	. . .	. . .
27	5740	0.1643	0.1805	. . .
27	5530	0.1654	0.1815	. . .
27	4350	0.1773	0.1943	. . .

Equation V-6 allows the calculation of the weight average molecular weight on the basis of light scattering intensities measured at various concentrations at a scatter angle of 90° and extrapolated to infinite dilution. The second osmotic virial coefficient is determined from the gradient of the plot Kc/R_{90} versus c.

Data obtained from light scattering measurements over the range of θ are interpreted with the aid of the Zimm plot. The weight average molecular weight M_w is determined by extrapolation to zero concentration and zero angle, the second osmotic virial coefficient from the slope of the concentration line at zero angle, and molecule size from the slope of the angle line at zero concentration.

The molecular weights determined by light-scattering measurements are in good agreement with those obtained from sedimentation and diffusion experiments. Similarly, the second osmotic virial coefficients calculated from light-scattering data agree within the limits of experimental error with those calculated from osmotic or from sedimentation and diffusion data (section V, 3, B, D).

End-to-end distances taken from the Zimm plots of the bisphenol A polycarbonate fractions investigated, however, were considerably in error due to the fact that these fractions all fell in the low molecular weight range where the interpretation of the graphs is quite difficult.

TABLE V-9

Molecular Chain End-to-End Distances Calculated from Light-Scattering Data (Intensity versus Angle θ) Measured on Solutions of Bisphenol A Polycarbonate Fractions

Molecular weight $\bar{M}_w$ from light scattering data	End-to-end distance h_s [Å]
61,000	400
122,000	530

D. Determination of Molecular Weights and Second Osmotic Virial Coefficients of Bisphenol A Polycarbonates in Dilute Solution by Osmometric Methods

Osmotic pressure data of macromolecular substances in dilute solution measured with an ideal semipermeable membrane can be used to calculate the number average molecular weight and the second osmotic virial coefficient.

Methylene chloride or tetrahydrofuran may be used as solvents in osmometric investigations of bisphenol A polycarbonates (1, 8). Breitenbach (19) and Meyerhoff (20) osmometers have been used, but other types are also suitable.

Some difficulties are encountered with cellulose membranes (e.g., Ultracella filters marketed by Membranfiltergesellschaft, Göttingen) because of their permeability to low molecular weight constituents. However, it is frequently possible to reduce the pore size of such membranes sufficiently by shrinking with or in suitable solvents (8). The osmotic pressure π is best measured between 20 and 30°C. From the ratio of the osmotic pressure to the concentration (π/c) at infinite dilution the osmotic molecular weight is calculated by using equation V-8. From the initial slope of π/c plotted versus c the second osmotic virial coefficient is determined.

$$(V-8) \qquad \pi/c = \frac{RT}{\overline{M}_{os}} + Bc + \ldots$$

Since for small values of c the π/c curve is linear within experimental error, it is not necessary to take higher virial coefficients into account. Based on osmotic pressures in dilute solutions, the average molecular weights ($\overline{M}_{os}$) of commercial bisphenol A polycarbonates vary from 20,-000 to 60,000, with materials sold for thermoplastic applications ranging from 20,000 to 23,000 and solvent casting material from 50,000 to 60,000.

Starting with high purity bisphenol A, the phosgenation method will produce, without difficulty, polycarbonates with molecular weights in excess of 500,000. There has been no commercial interest so far, however, in polycarbonates with molecular weights above 60,000, since above this number solution and melt viscosities become too high for economical processing.

A summary of molecular weights and second osmotic virial coefficients determined by osmometric investigation of various bisphenol A polycarbonate fractions in dilute solution is presented in Table V-10 (8).

The value of the second osmotic virial coefficient decreases with increasing molecular weight. Extrapolation to a molecular weight of 1000, corresponding approximately to the length of a random coiled chain, according to Kuhn, gives coefficients of $\overline{B} = 5.2 \times 10^{-7}$ [erg cm³/g²] for methylene chloride and $\overline{B} = 4.8 \times 10^{-7}$ [erg cm³/g²] for tetrahydrofuran. These values are comparable with those determined for polymethyl-

TABLE V-10

Molecular Weights and Second Osmotic Virial Coefficients of Various Bisphenol A Polycarbonate Fractions Determined by Osmometric Measurements at 27 [°C]

Tetrahydrofuran		Methylene chloride	
$\bar{M}_{os}$	$\bar{B} \times 10^7$ [erg cm^3/g^2]	$\bar{M}_{os}$	$\bar{B} \times 10^7$ [erg cm^3/g^2]
23,900	2.5	23,600	3.9
35,000	3.2	35,000	3.1
49,000	2.5	49,000	3.3
53,000	2.4	57,000	3.4
77,000	2.1	. . .	. . .
92,000	1.7	107,000	2.7
. . .	. . .	182,000	2.9

methacrylate in acetone and polystyrene in benzene and are in agreement with those calculated by G. V. Schulz (21) for rigid rods.

For chloroform solutions of bisphenol A polycarbonate the second osmotic virial coefficient disappears at a temperature of 20°C. This means that at this temperature chloroform is a pseudoideal solvent for the polycarbonate (18).

E.   Solution Viscosities of Bisphenol A Polycarbonates

The easiest method for characterizing polycarbonates, hence the one most frequently used in production control, is a determination of the viscosity of dilute solutions. Once calibrated via absolute methods, solution viscosity may also be used to calculate average molecular weight. In conjunction with sedimentation and diffusion measurements solution viscosity data furthermore enable us to make certain deductions about the shape of the molecules in solution.

A number of different solvents, including 1,1,2,2-tetrachloroethane, chloroform, cis-dichloroethylene, 1,1,2-trichloroethane, methylene chloride, 1,4-dioxane, and tetrahydrofuran, are suitable for solution viscosity measurements. The preference usually goes to methylene chloride.

In the interest of simplicity capillary viscometers of the Ubbelohde or Ostwald types are used. With these types of apparatus it is not necessary to extrapolate the measured viscosities to zero shear rate as long as the shear gradient is kept below 1500/sec.

Polycarbonates may be characterized by their viscosity ratio η/η_0. defined as the ratio of the solution viscosity to that of the pure solvent or, when the same viscometer is used, as the ratio of the time required to pass a certain amount of solution to the time needed to pass an equal amount of solvent. For comparable results in production control it is necessary to standardize on a certain solution concentration and temperature. Most laboratories use a solution containing 0.005 g/ml of polycarbonate at 25°C.

To obtain a relationship between solution viscosity and molecular weight, the limiting viscosity number $[\eta]$, defined as the limiting value of the viscosity number $(\eta - \eta_0)/\eta_0 c$ at infinite dilution, is calculated

$$\text{(V-9)} \qquad [\eta] = \lim_{\substack{c \to 0 \\ \tau \to 0}} \left(\frac{\eta - \eta_0}{\eta_0 c} \right)$$

To determine exactly the limiting viscosity number, it is necessary to measure the viscosity ratio η/η_0 over a range of concentrations and extrapolate the viscosity number to zero concentration.

However, empirical relationships have been formulated which make it possible to calculate the limiting viscosity number from a single pair of viscosity-concentration values for bisphenol A polycarbonate solutions in methylene chloride at 20 or 25°C, as long as the concentration does not significantly exceed 0.01 g/ml.

Both the Schulz-Blaschke equation (22)

$$\text{(V-10)} \qquad \frac{\eta - \eta_0}{\eta_0 c} = [\eta] + K_{SB} \frac{\eta - \eta_0}{\eta_0} \cdot [\eta]$$

and the Huggins correlation (23)

$$\text{(V-11)} \qquad \frac{\eta - \eta_0}{\eta_0 c} = [\eta] + K_H [\eta]^2 c$$

have been used for this purpose. In these equations K_{SB} and K_H are constants specific to the polymer/solvent system under consideration. Table V-11 summarizes these constants to the extent that they have been ascertained so far.

The values of K_H and K_{SB} do not change, within experimental error, with changes of either molecular weight or temperature (20–25°C). If it can be assumed that only linear macromolecules are present in the solution, the limiting viscosity number can be "calibrated" by means of one of the absolute methods and then used for molecular weight determinations on the basis of solution viscosity measurements. Bisphenol A polycarbonate has a linear structure, provided the bisphenol A used in its

TABLE V-11

System Constants K_H and K_{SB} for Calculating the Limiting Viscosity Number
of a Bisphenol A Polycarbonate from a Single Pair of Solution Viscosity Data

Solvent	K_{SB}	K_H	Reference
Methylene chloride	0.30	0.43	(8)
Chloroform	. . .	0.29	(15)
Tetrahydrofuran	0.36	0.47	(8)

manufacture was of high purity, in particular essentially free of tris- and
polyphenols (section IV, 1, A, 1), and provided further that if the ester
exchange process was used (section III, 3, A, 4) too high a concentration
of some strongly alkaline ester exchange catalyst was not employed.

To calculate the molecular weight from the limiting viscosity number,
the Staudinger-Kuhn correlation is used:

$$(V\text{-}12) \qquad\qquad [\eta] = KM^\alpha$$

Table V-12 lists the constants K and exponents α which have so far
been ascertained by experimentally determining limiting viscosity numbers of various bisphenol A polycarbonates of known molecular weight.
These numbers require the concentration to be expressed in grams per
milliliter, corresponding to the dimension milliliters per gram used for the
limiting viscosity number.

Chloroform at 20°C is a pseudoideal solvent for bisphenol A polycarbonate (section V, 3, D). In this borderline case the limiting viscosity
number is directly proportional to the square root of the molecular weight
(18). The same is true for a mixture of 80 volume per cent chloroform and
20 volume per cent methanol at 18°C (15).

F.   Molecular Dimensions of Bisphenol A Polycarbonate in Solution as Determined by Sedimentation, Diffusion, and Viscosity Measurements

Both light-scattering data (section V, 3, C) and experimentally determined frictional characteristics, the latter interpreted via the hydrodynamic correlations of Kirkwood-Riseman (24) and Debye-Bueche-
Peterlin (25), can be used to calculate dimensions of the randomly coiled
polycarbonate chain and thus develop information about the mobility of
the polymer molecule in solution.

If frictional data developed on tetrahydrofuran solutions of bisphenol
A polycarbonates are treated by the two methods mentioned, consistently

TABLE V-12

Constants in the Staudinger-Kuhn Correlation for the Determination of Molecular Weights of Bisphenol A Polycarbonate Fractions from Limiting Viscosity Numbers at 20°C

Solvent	Molecular weight determined by	Calibrated range	K	α	Reference
Methylene chloride	Sedimentation Diffusion Light-scattering	$8 \times 10^3\text{–}2.7 \times 10^5$	1.11×10^{-2}	0.82	(8)
Methylene chloride	Light-scattering	$1.3 \times 10^4\text{–}8 \times 10^4$	1.11×10^{-2}	0.82	(11)
Methylene chloride	Osmometry	$2.5 \times 10^4\text{–}1 \times 10^5$	1.23×10^{-2}	0.83	(1)
Methylene chloride	Osmometry Light-scattering	$2.2 \times 10^4\text{–}2 \times 10^5$	0.92×10^{-3}	0.87	(8)
Chloroform	Light-scattering	$1.5 \times 10^4\text{–}6 \times 10^4$	2.77×10^{-1}	0.50	(18)
Dioxane	Light-scattering	$1 \times 10^4\text{–}4 \times 10^5$	5.54×10^{-2}	0.67	(5)
Tetrahydrofuran	Sedimentation Diffusion Light-scattering	$8 \times 10^3\text{–}2.7 \times 10^5$	3.99×10^{-2}	0.70	(8)

different results are obtained in that end-to-end chain distances calculated according to Kirkwood-Riseman are always smaller than those calculated according to Debye-Bueche-Peterlin (8).

When interpreting data developed with the better solvent methylene chloride, however, the two methods yield end-to-end distances that agree well with each other and also with values determined by light-scattering experiments.

The following empirical equations relate the end-to-end distance h_S of a bisphenol A polycarbonate molecule (in Å) in methylene chloride or tetrahydrofuran solution, respectively, to the molecular weight (8):

(V-13)   Methylene chloride $h_S = 0.66 M_{\eta(s,D)}^{0.58}$

(V-14)   Tetrahydrofuran $h_S = 1.04 M_{\eta(s,D)}^{0.53}$

As is to be expected, the exponent is larger for methylene chloride, as it is the better solvent and has a larger second osmotic virial coefficient.

Chirico (18) calculated the root of the mean-square radius of gyration $\sqrt{(\bar{r}_0)^2}$ from the correlation given by Fox and Flory (26). This can be done because at 20° chloroform is a pseudoideal solvent for the polycarbonate. The result is the following equation in centimeters:

(V-15) $$\sqrt{(\bar{r}_0)^2} = 0.988 \times 10^{-8} M_w^{0.5}$$

Thus for a molecular weight of 50,000 the mean radius of gyration in chloroform solution at 20°C is calculated to 240 [Å]. By comparison, end-to-end distances of 351 [Å] and 304 [Å] are calculated from (V-13) and (V-14) for the same molecular weight polycarbonate in methylene chloride and tetrahydrofuran solution, respectively. These results confirm the expectation that coil dimensions in solution increase with an increase in solvent power, i.e., with increasing second osmotic virial coefficient.

Having experimentally determined the end-to-end distances for specific bisphenol A polycarbonate fractions in tetrahydrofuran and methylene chloride solutions, Schulz and Horbach (8) used the correlation of Zimm, Stockmayer, and Fixman (27) to calculate the undisturbed end-to-end distances h_0 for a solvent with a zero second osmotic virial coefficient. A comparison of the h_0 values obtained with those reported for polymethylmethacrylates of the same molecular weight indicates that in the absence of a solvent interaction effect (i.e., in the random flight configuration) the extension of the polycarbonate molecule is 2.75 times that of the polymethylmethacrylate chain. They attribute this to the greater length of the base unit, the rotational freedom of the polycarbonate molecule being greater than that of polymethylmethacrylate.

Chirico (18) has calculated the "degree of stiffness" of the polycarbonate molecule in chloroform solution at 20°C, using the correlation presented by Chinai, Scherer, Bondurant, and Levi (28). A comparison of the "degree of stiffness" calculated for a molecular weight of 50,000 with those of polystyrene and polymethylmethacrylate confirms the conclusions reached by Schulz and Horbach (8) that the flexibility of the polycarbonate molecule in solution is greater than that of vinyl polymers of equal molecular weight, notwithstanding the fact that it occupies a larger "volume."

Since the hydrodynamic resistance of the macromolecule in solution determines the dilute solution viscosity, bisphenol A polycarbonate with its large coil diameter displays a $[\eta]$-M relationship which, in spite of its great flexibility, puts it between the cellulose derivatives for very restricted rotation and the polyvinyls (8).

It would be of great interest to extend these investigations to polycarbonates based on 4,4'-dihydroxy-diphenyl methane derivatives with bulky substituents introduced on the central C-atom in order to determine whether hindrances to rotation of the aromatic groups with respect to the central carbon atom, which lead to higher melting ranges and second-order transition temperatures (section V, 2), will also effect the flexibility of the macromolecule in solution.

4. MELT VISCOSITY OF BISPHENOL A POLYCARBONATE

Factors affecting the melt viscosities of macromolecular substances are chemical composition, molecular structure, molecular weight, molecular weight distribution, temperature, the magnitude of shear stress, and rate of shear. The basic requirement for a thermoplastic material is that at a molecular weight which produces parts with desirable physical properties it must, over a temperature range somewhere between melting point and decomposition temperature, display a melt viscosity that makes it suitable for processing on the equipment common in plastics technology, such as injection molding machines and extruders.

The bisphenol A polycarbonate retains its stability for many hours in the molten state at temperatures up to 300°C (1). For short periods it will withstand temperatures up to 320°C. Above 330°C decomposition sets in, evidenced by discoloration, chain degradation, a release of carbon dioxide, and the formation of unspecified decomposition products. Since even small amounts of water in the polycarbonate melt will cause degradation accompanied by a release of CO_2, it is imperative that solid polycarbonate be dried to a moisture content below 0.01% before melting. The absence of atmospheric oxygen is also a requirement, since oxygen causes discoloration and perhaps promotes crosslinking reactions (section III, 3, A, 7, B). The entire relatively wide temperature range from 230 to 320°C is available for thermoplastic processing.

Figure V-2 shows the melt viscosity η_m in poise of a bisphenol A polycarbonate ($M_{\eta(S,D)} = 33,000$), as a function of time and temperature.

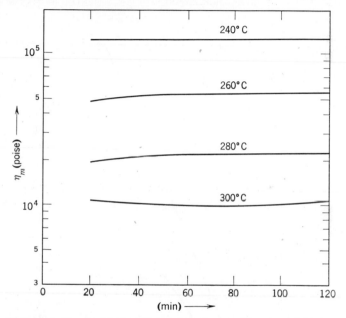

Fig. V-2. Melt viscosity of a bisphenol A polycarbonate $M_{\eta(S,D)} = 33,000$ versus time and temperature.

In the range between 240 and 300°C the melt viscosity of this polycarbonate extends from 100,000 to 10,000 poise, which is rather high compared to other thermoplastics. This high-melt viscosity is probably due to limited mobility of the macromolecules in the melt caused by interlocking of molecular chains and hindered rotation of the aromatic rings with respect to the central C-atom of the bisphenol A unit (section V, 2 and V, 5). The variation of melt viscosity with temperature can be used to calculate an activation energy for viscous flow; this varies with shear rate, decreasing from 23.5 kcal/mole at a shear rate of 3 sec⁻¹ to 16.4 kcal/mole, as the shear rate is raised to 100 sec⁻¹. Extrapolated to zero shear rate, this activation energy is about 26–30 kcal/mole, a fairly high value compared to other polymers. This again points to the rigidity of the polycarbonate molecule in the melt (11).

The magnitude of shear stress leaves the melt viscosity of bisphenol A polycarbonate almost unaffected over the entire range from 0 to 12×10^5 dyne/cm² (29).

Shear stresses measured as a function of shear rate have given evidence that above 280°C molten polycarbonate is essentially a Newtonian liquid.

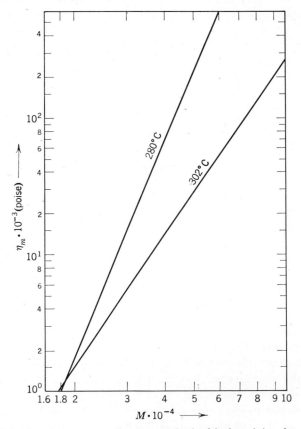

Fig. V-3. Melt viscosity versus molecular weight for bisphenol A polycarbonates at 280 and 302°C.

At lower temperatures structural viscosity is observed. The melt viscosity then decreases with increasing shear rate (11). Figure V-3 illustrates the relationship between melt viscosity and molecular weight.

Melt viscosities of bisphenol A polycarbonates with molecular weights M_w ranging from 13,000 to 80,000 were measured by Baumann and Steingiser (11) with a capillary rheometer at a temperature of 302°C and a shear stress of 2.63×10^5 dyne/cm²; the following correlations were obtained:

(V-16) $$\eta_{m(302°C)} = 1.862 \times 10^{-11} \times M_w^{3.23}$$
$$\log \eta_{m(302°C)} = 3.23 \times \log M_w - 10.73$$

Melt viscosities measured at the Farbenfabriken Bayer, Uerdingen, Physical Laboratory, at 280°C and at 0.764×10^5 dyne/cm² shear stress on ester exchange bisphenol A polycarbonates, ranging from 18,000 to 40,000 in molecular weight, are expressed by

(V-17) $$\eta_{m(280°C)} = 2.596 \times 10^{-20} \times M_w^{5.306}$$
$$\log \eta_{m(280°C)} = 5.306 \times \log M_w - 19.59$$

Comparative melt viscosity data on bisphenol A polycarbonates with different molecular weight distributions have shown that for a given average molecular weight the melt viscosity decreases with increasing polymer uniformity (11).

Injection molding of bisphenol A polycarbonate is rendered somewhat difficult by the high-melt viscosity. It is necessary to take full advantage of the high thermal stability of the material if, in the interest of favorable mechanical properties, polycarbonates of sufficiently high molecular weights are to be processed by this method.

5. CRYSTAL STRUCTURE AND MORPHOLOGY OF BISPHENOL A POLYCARBONATE IN THE NONSTRETCHED AND STRETCHED STATES

The crystallizability of bisphenol A polycarbonate varies with molecular weight and also to some extent with molecular weight distribution. Low molecular products will crystallize more easily and completely than those of high molecular weight. Polycarbonate copolymers obtained by replacing the bisphenol A in part with a 4,4'-dihydroxy-diphenyl alkane of unsymmetrical structure or one with bulky substituents introduced on the central C-atom display a reduced tendency to crystallize. Partially replacing the carbonic acid residues with residues of unsymmetrical aromatic dicarboxylic acid has the same effect.

Parts made from bisphenol A polycarbonates having molecular weights M_w above 25,000, either by cooling from the melt or by rapid evaporation of the solvent from a solution, are clear and transparent. X-ray examination (30), however, reveals that these clear and transparent articles, produced commercially by thermoplastic methods (e.g., injection molded parts) or solution casting (e.g., film) are not entirely amorphous. They have a structure comparable to that of a subcooled liquid (glass state), by which short-range order begins to be supplemented with regularity extending over larger distances. Since the ordered regions are considerably smaller than the wavelengths of visible light, the parts appear optically clear.

In X-ray analysis the width at half or maximum intensity of the radial intensity curves in Debye-Scherrer diagram provides a ready estimate of the degree of molecular order (30). For highly amorphous pieces of bisphenol A polycarbonate this width at half of maximum intensity, measured in terms of the Bragg angle θ, is approximately 3.5°; for commercially cast film and injection molded parts it varies between 2.8 and 3.2°. These numbers were determined after subtracting background scattering measured between $\theta = 2.5$ to 17.5° (31).

Determining that portion of the scattering intensity which is attributable to ordered areas within the material allows an estimate of the volume fraction of polymer present in an ordered state. For commercial parts these estimates range from 10 to 40%. This puts bisphenol A polycarbonate between the largely amorphous plastics, such as PVC, and the highly crystalline polymers, such as polyaminocaproic acid.

A particularly simple process for radiographic determination of the crystallinity of bisphenol A polycarbonates has been suggested by Hermans and Weidinger (32). Under standardized conditions they determine the scattered intensity with a deflection angle of $2\theta = 12.2°$ on a partially crystalline and amorphous sample and calculate the amorphous portion from the ratio of the intensities. This kind of evaluation is based on the assumption that the $2\theta = 12.2°$ the share of the crystalline portion in total scattering is virtually zero.

In the solid state crystallization of this polycarbonate is inhibited to such a degree that the amount of molecular ordering established during the manufacturing operation is essentially retained over the entire temperature range from -100 to $+149°$C. At room temperatures parts consequently maintain indefinitely the physical properties resulting from the glasslike state.

Physical methods have disclosed a number of higher order transition temperatures below the second-order transition temperature of 149°C. None of these transitions, however, shows effects discernible either in the X-ray diagram or by density measurements.

In order to obtain the polycarbonate in a highly crystalline state, it is necessary to increase the mobility of the macromolecules in the solid

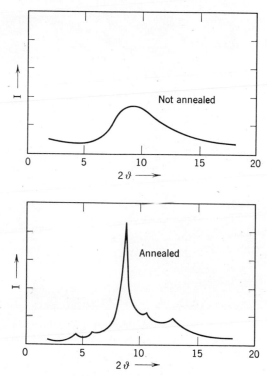

Fig. V-4. Changes in the radial intensity curves of Debye-Scherrer diagrams of an injection molded part of bisphenol A polycarbonate induced by holding at 190°C for two weeks ($M\eta_{(s,D)} = 34{,}000$).

by suitable means for a sufficient period of time. This may be accomplished by holding for an extended period at a temperature above the second-order transition temperature but below the melting range. At 190°C bisphenol A polycarbonates require holding times in the order of days or even weeks.

The crystallization of a largely amorphous bisphenol A polycarbonate part shows the alteration of the width at half of maximum intensity after two weeks of annealing at 190°C under dry nitrogen as illustrated in Figure V-4.

The same effect can be achieved by passing very slowly through the temperature zone between range and second-order transition temperature when the polycarbonate is cooled from the melt. In either case it is imperative to keep away all traces of moisture and oxygen; otherwise

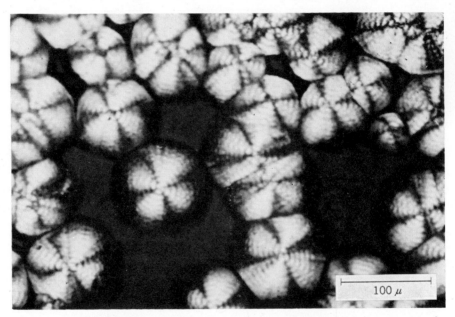

Fig. V-5. Spherulites in a bisphenol A polycarbonate film ($M\eta_{(s,D)} = 34,000$) obtained by slow evaporation from methylene chloride solution (conventional photomicrograph, cross polarizers).

degradation and discoloring is inevitable. Highly crystalline polycarbonate specimens can also be obtained by treating parts with swelling agents (e.g., acetone) or solvent vapors by extremely slow evaporation of the solvent from dilute solutions or by slow cooling of polycarbonate solutions in substances that are solvents at elevated temperature only (e.g., toluene).

With any one of these methods the polycarbonate is held long enough in a state in which small amounts of solvent within the solid material increase the mobility of the macromolecules to the point at which crystallites can be formed.

Rapid isolation of polycarbonates from solution by evaporation of the solvent, such as is encountered in solvent casting of film, can also be made to yield highly crystalline product if casting is done from a mixture containing besides a good solvent, such as methylene chloride, small amounts of higher boiling poor solvents, swelling agents, or nonsolvents. For instance, a mixture of 94% (by weight) of methylene chloride and 6% of di-*n*-butyl ether is quite effective with bisphenol A polycarbonate (33).

Fig. V-6. Spherulites in a bisphenol A polycarbonate film ($M\eta$ $_{(s,D)}$ = 34,000) after annealing for eight days at 190°C (electron photomicrograph of a carbon-platinum surface replica after partial destruction of the polycarbonate).

G. Kämpf (34) has shown that morphological structures of crystallized bisphenol A polycarbonate can be observed under the conventional and the electron microscope (Figs. V-5 through V-8) in the form of elementary structures (lamellae, fibrils) and composite structures (spherulites).

The morphological structures displayed in Figures V-5, 6, 7, and 8 are eloquent proof that as far as the formation of elementary and composite structures is concerned bisphenol A polycarbonate behaves in a manner no different from other easily crystallizable polymers, such as polyethylene or polyaminocaproic acid (35), as soon as macromolecule mobility is artificially increased.

The composite structures obtained by Makavuk, Koslov, and Kargin (36), who crystallized bisphenol A polycarbonate from solution by various methods, are largely in agreement with those described by Kämpf. The fibril bundles they observed had to be interpreted as intermediate steps in the formation of spherulites. More effective treatment would in these cases also have led to spherulites visible under the conventional

Fig. V-7. Fibril bundles preceding spherulite formation, obtained by slow cooling of a hot bisphenol A polycarbonate [$M\eta_{(s,D)} = 34,000$] solution in toluene (electron photomicrograph after oblique vaporization with Pt-Pd).

microscope. However, the theory advanced by the authors that the desirable mechanical properties of bisphenol A polycarbonate might be due to the "reinforced concrete" type structure approximated by the combination of fibrils and amorphous regions and/or voids is not likely to be correct, since the fibril structure is not originally present in injection molded parts and solvent cast film but appears only after special treatment designed to induce crystallization.

At temperatures below the second-order transition temperature bisphenol A polycarbonate may be cold-drawn to about twice its original length by which the macromolecules are oriented parallel to the direction of stress; the process is accompanied by necking. Birefringence increases as a result of stretching, but X-ray diffraction patterns do not indicate an increase in crystallinity.

Considerably higher draw ratios (up to 10) and a greater degree of orientation may be realized at temperatures between the second-order transition temperature and the melting range. At these temperatures a

Fig. V-8. Lamella structure in a film of bisphenol A polycarbonate ($M_{\eta(s,D)} = $ 34,000) after annealing for eight days at 190°C (electron photomicrograph of a surface replica after complete destruction of the polycarbonate).

certain amount of thermoplastic deformation is superimposed over the stretching effect so that no arrest point is observed (1). Again there is usually no gain in crystallinity. Only within a very narrow temperature range, in which a plot of the dielectric loss angle tan δ shows a maximum, is it possible to stretch polycarbonate film of fibers through a specific draw ratio characterized by a definite arrest point to a high degree of orientation and simultaneously "lock in" the oriented state by crystallization (37).

Bisphenol A polycarbonate film and fibers can undergo this stretching with a draw ratio of 4:1 and a definite arrest point at temperatures around 186°C. The resulting oriented and crystallized materials display extremely good mechanical properties (section V, 6), considerably reduced solubility and swellability in organic solvents, and a higher melting range. The oriented state is retained in spite of heating to temperatures close to the melting range. Particularly rapid and thorough crystallization upon stretching was observed on polycarbonates if the original material was not in the glasslike state but rather already somewhat crystallized (33).

It appears that in this case the orientation of the macromolecules in the direction of applied stress causes only a partial loss of established

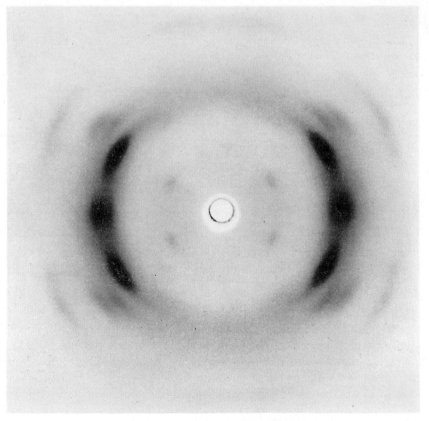

Fig. V-9. Fiber diagram of an oriented and crystallized bisphenol A polycarbonate film.

crystalline order, with the remaining ordered regions serving as nuclei for subsequent thorough crystallization of the oriented molecules. Polycarbonate products of an essentially two-dimensional nature will attain optimum properties by orientation and crystallization if stretched in two directions at right angles to each other (38).

An analysis of the crystal structure of bisphenol A polycarbonate was made by Prietzschk (30) with the aid of fiber and escillation diagrams (Fig. V-9) of oriented crystallized film.

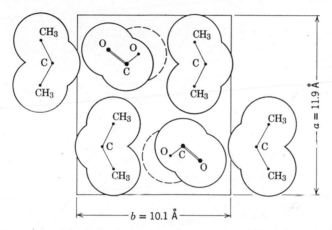

Fig. V-10. Base plane of the unit cell of bisphenol A polycarbonate in the oriented and crystallized state.

Figure V-10 shows the base plane of the unit cell, Figure V-11 the bc-plane, and Figure V-12 the position of the macromolecules in the unit cell of an oriented crystallized bisphenol A polycarbonate.

The identity distance in the fiber direction is 21.5 Å. The crystallite length is small and has been estimated to be roughly six times the identity distance, i.e., approximately 120 Å.

The lattice is orthorhombic, and the unit cell dimensions perpendicular to the stress direction are $a = 11.9$ Å and $b = 10.1$ Å. The lattice constant in the fiber direction is identical with the identity distance, i.e., 21.5 Å.

The space group arrangement D_2 3 appears the most likely, but the lower groups D_2 2 and D_2 1 also are not impossible.

Four molecular chains, each containing two base units, extend through a unit cell. The calculated X-ray density of the crystallites is 1.30 g/ml, which is 8% higher than the measured polymer density of 1.20 g/ml. By

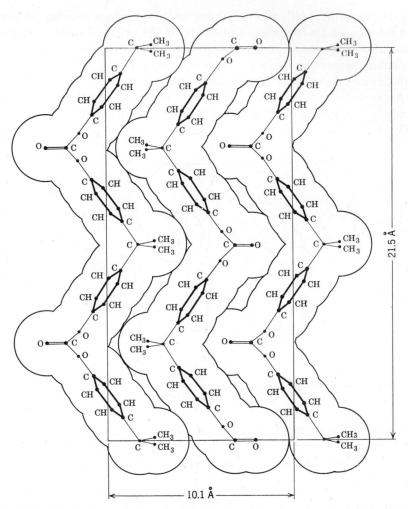

Fig. V-11· The *bc*-plane of the unit cell of bisphenol A polycarbonate in the oriented and crystallized state.

comparison, the difference between the calculated crystal density and the (superficial) macroscopic density is smaller for polyaminocaproic acid (6%) and hydrated cellulose (5%), which implies that the macromolecules are not so densely packed in the amorphous regions.

Table V-13 summarizes the densities of various aromatic polycarbonates, measured on solvent cast film samples by the suspension method in sodium nitrite solution at 25°C (1,2). It can be seen that hindered rotation

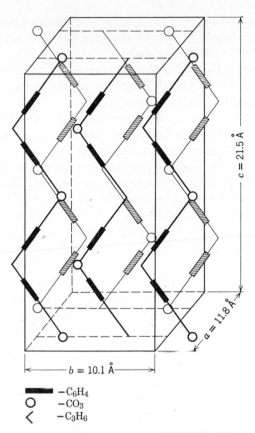

$c = 21.5$ Å

$a = 11.8$ Å

$b = 10.1$ Å

▬	$-C_6H_4$
◯	$-CO_3$
‹	$-C_3H_6$

Fig. V-12. Position of the macromolecules in the unit cell of bisphenol A polycarbonate in the oriented and crystallized state.

of the aromatic groups with regard to the central carbon atom caused by bulky substituents in many cases causes a marked decrease in the density of the polycarbonate. Substituents introduced on the aromatic groups lead to polycarbonates of comparatively high density. Irregular behavior is again noted for polycarbonates, in which the central C-atom is either part of a cycloaliphatic ring or substituted with an aryl; their density is found to be relatively high.

The macromolecule in the crystal lattice most likely has the shape of a zig-zag chain, with directional changes at the central C-atom of the

bisphenol A unit and at the —O— $\overset{\overset{\text{O}}{\|}}{\text{C}}$ —O— group (Fig. V-13).

X-ray studies of solvent cast bisphenol A polycarbonate film have shown a certain amount of planar (surface parallel) orientation of the aromatic rings in the molecular chain.

The mechanism involved in the crystallization of bisphenol A polycarbonate appears to be the principle of least volume rather than an effect of directional intermolecular forces (30).

The relative immobility of the macromolecules within the solid material, caused by the interlocking of molecular chains (Fig. V-11) in a manner that requires the distance between chains to increase considerably before a sliding motion becomes possible, is responsible for the fact that the crystallization of this polycarbonate is strongly inhibited. In addition, steric hindrance to free rotation of the aromatic rings relative to the central C-atom of the bisphenol A unit due to the methyl substituents is effective. Polycarbonates based on 4,4'-dihydroxy-diphenyl compounds with unrestricted rotation relative to the central C-atom, e.g., 4,4'-dihydroxy-diphenyl methane, -1,2-ethane, -1,10-decane, 4,4'-dihydroxy-diphenyl ethers, and 4,4'-dihydroxy-diphenyl sulfide, crystallize rapidly and to a high degree. Solid parts produced by cooling such materials from the molten state are opaque rather than transparent because of

TABLE V-13
Densities of Aromatic Polycarbonates

Polycarbonate based on	$D_{25°C}$ [g/ml]
4,4-Dihydroxy-diphenyl-1,1-ethane	1.22
" " -1,1-butane	1.17
" " -1,1-isobutane	1.18
" " -1,1-cyclopentane	1.21
" " -1,1-cyclohexane	1.20
" " -2,2-propane	1.20
" " -2,2-butane	1.18
" " -2,2-pentane	1.13
" " -2,2-(4-methyl)-pentane	1.14
" " -4,4-heptane	1.16
4,4'-Dihydroxy-triphenyl-2,2,2-ethane	1.21
4,4'-Dihydroxy-tetraphenyl-methane	1.27
4,4'-Dihydroxy-3,3',5,5'-tetrachloro-diphenyl-2,2-propane	1.24
4,4'-Dihydroxy-3,3',5,5'-tetrachloro-diphenyl-1,1-cyclohexane	1.38
4,4'-Dihydroxy-3,3'-dimethyl-diphenyl-2,2-propane	1.22

Fig. V-13. Part of a bisphenol A polycarbonate macromolecule (Stuart-Briegleb model).

the large size of the crystallites formed. Bulky substituents on the central C-atom of 4,4'-dihydroxy-diphenyl methane derivatives, on the other hand, lead to polycarbonates with even more inhibited crystallinity compared to bisphenol A polycarbonate (3).

6. MECHANICAL AND THERMAL PROPERTIES AND PROPERTIES UNDER DYNAMIC CONDITIONS OF BISPHENOL A POLYCARBONATE

The usefulness of plastic parts is, for a variety of applications, determined by a large number of properties, only few of which can be characterized by well-defined physical values. The mechanical properties of finished parts as determined or effected by exposure conditions, e.g., temperature and humidity, method of manufacture, shape, and possibly size of the individual item, are always of great importance in screening potential areas of application for a new product. Particularly in the United States and Germany, these have been extensively studied for commercial bisphenol A polycarbonates, using established methods and standardized specimens (1 through 5, 29, 39, 40 through 49). Almost all test work has been done on injection molded pieces or on extruded or solvent cast film. Only exploratory data are available for stretched and crystallized polycarbonate fibers. Standard material specifications for injection molding grade polycarbonate (Type 300) exist (50).

Table V-14 summarizes the mechanical properties of injection-molded commercial bisphenol A polycarbonates as determined by United States and German standard methods (39,47).

TABLE V-14

Mechanical Properties of Injection-Molded Bisphenol A Polycarbonate

Property	Method DIN No.	Value	Property	Method ASTM No.	Value
Density [g/ml]	53 479	1.20	Impact strength (izod) notched [ft·lb/in]	D-256 $(1/2'' \times 1/4'')$ $(1/2'' \times 1/8'')$	2-3 12-16
Flexural strength [kg/cm²]	53 452	1100-1200	Tensile yield strength [psi]	D-638	8000-9000
Impact strength [cm·kg/cm²]	53 453	100% unbroken	Elongation, at yield [%]	D-638	5-7
Impact strength (notched) [cm·kg/cm²]	53 453	> 20	Elongation, ultimate [%]	D-638	60-100
Compressive strength [kg/cm²]	53 454	790-840	Compressive strength at yield point [psi]	D-695	12,000
Ball indentations hardness of plastics [kg/cm²] 10s 60s	DIN-Entwurf 53 456	900-1050 870-1000			
Ball indentations hardness of plastics [kg/mm²]	DIN-Vornorm 53 456	Hc 10.6	Deformation under load [%]	D-621	0.14
Tensile yield strength [kg/cm²]	53 455	625	Flexural strength [psi]	D-790	11,000-13,000
Elongation [%] at yield ultimate	53 455 53 455	5-7 > 60	Modulus of elasticity tension [psi]	D-638	$2.8-3.2 \cdot 10^5$
Modulus of elasticity [kg/cm²]		22-25,000	Flexural [psi] Rockwell hardness	D-790 D-785	$3.2-3.4 \cdot 10^5$ R-115

The mechanical properties of bisphenol A polycarbonate are dependent on the molecular weight. Materials having an average molecular weight M_w below 10,000 are brittle and will not form films· If M_w is between 10,000 and about 25,000, low strength parts are obtained (51). The strength values given in Table V-14 are all measured on specimens having molecular weights M_w between 32,000 and 35,000. A further increase in molecular weight no longer is accompanied by a significant improvement in mechanical properties, whereas at the same time thermo-

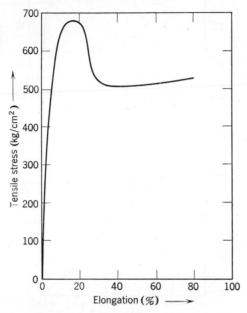

Fig. V-14. Stress-strain diagram of a bisphenol A polycarbonate specimen according to DIN 53,371.

plastic processing on injection-molding equipment becomes increasingly difficult because of the rapid rise in melt viscosity with increasing molecular weight (5). In general, the values summarized in this table present the picture of a hard and tough plastic material with very desirable mechanical properties.

Moisture content, which in the open atmosphere reaches a maximum value of 0.20%, does not affect the mechanical properties.

The toughness of the material is maintained even in the face of extremely fast acting external forces. This is well documented by the fact

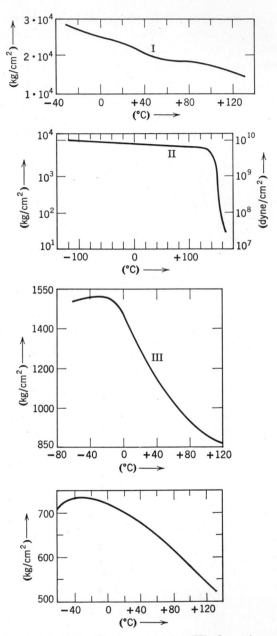

Fig. V-15. Modulus of elasticity (I), shear modulus (II), flexural strength (III), and tensile strength (IV) of injection-molded bisphenol A polycarbonate.

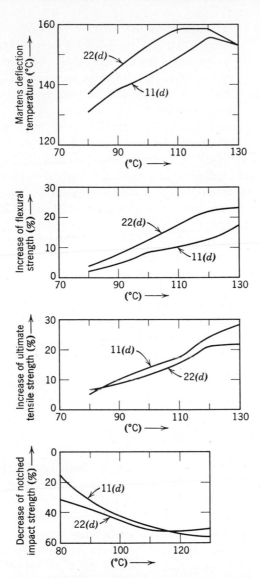

Fig. V-16. Changes in the Martens deflection temperature (Martens test), flexural strength, ultimate tensile strength, and notched impact strength of injection-molded bisphenol A polycarbonate samples as a result of holding at elevated temperatures for various periods of time.

that the impact of a bullet does not shatter polycarbonate plate as it does many other plastics (39). The stress-strain curve of a test specimen (Fig. V-14) shows essentially linear reversible elongation up to high stress values, the type of behavior common to most metals (39). As a result, the dimensional stability of the polycarbonate is excellent; its tendency to cold flow is very low.

A sample held under 220 kg/cm^2 tensile stress for a one-year period showed no measurable plastic deformation (39).

The glasslike structure of molded parts (section V, 5), together with their strongly inhibited crystallization and high second-order transition temperature, allow this polycarbonate to maintain its toughness over an unusually wide temperature range of about −150 to +150°C (52).

The curves of modulus of elasticity, flexural strength, and shear modulus versus temperature of injection-molded bisphenol A polycarbonate parts are shown in Figure V-15 (39,52).

Parts injection-molded from bisphenol A polycarbonate display favorable mechanical properties and high dimensional stability over a temperature range of more than 200°C.

As a result of the fact that the crystallization tendency of bisphenol A polycarbonate is very low indeed, mechanical properties of parts stored at room temperature remain unchanged indefinitely.

Holding parts at temperatures between 110 and 130°C, i.e., below the second-order transition temperature, for extended periods of time causes a gradual change of the mechanical properties. Increases are observed in the Martens deflection temperature (Martens test), flexural strength, and ultimate tensile strength, while the notched impact strength is reduced (Fig. V-16).

This slight stiffening of the specimens without loss of the basic toughness of the material is accompanied neither by an increase in density nor by any change in the X-ray diffraction picture. This means that it can be explained only in terms of a rearrangement of ordered regions that already exist. This process is sometimes referred to as "physical crosslinking" and is reversible. A temperature increase toward the second-order transition temperature makes most of its effects disappear, whereas one into the melting range makes all of its effects disappear.

Table V-15 summarizes the most important thermal properties of bisphenol A polycarbonate determined on injection-molded commercial materials by United States and German test methods (39,47).

A plot of thermal conductivity versus temperature of bisphenol A polycarbonate, measured on injection-molded panels, is shown in Figure

TABLE V-15

Thermal Properties of Injection-Molded Bisphenol A Polycarbonate

Property	Method	Value	Property	ASTM method	Value
Melting temperature [°C]	Kofler	220–230	Melting temperature [°F]		425–440
Deflection temperature			Crystalline melting temperature [°F]		505
MARTENS [°C]	DIN 53,458	115–127			
VICAT [°C]	VDE 0302	164–166			
Thermal conductivity [kcal/m·hr·°C]	VDE 0304 section 1, according to Erk	0.17	Deflection temperature under load [°F]	D 648	
			264 psi		280
			66 psi		290
Specific heat [kcal/kg·°C]		0.28	Specific heat [cal/°C·g]		0.28
Average linear coefficient of expansion between 25 and 85°C, per °C	VDE 0304 section 1	60×10^{-6}	Coefficient of linear thermal expansion [in/in·°C] (32°–140°F)	D 696	3.9×10^{-5}
Maximum service temperature [°C]		135			
Brittleness temperature [°C]		Below −100	Flammability	D 635	Self extinguishing

V-17 (53). Molded parts made of bisphenol A polycarbonate which have been stretched in one direction show increased thermal conductivity and reduced thermal expansion in the direction of stretching (54).

In addition to the second-order transition temperature, a higher order transition temperature around 110–115°C is indicated by discontinuities in the plots of bisphenol A polycarbonate specific heat and specific volume versus temperature (Fig. V-18) (55). This is the temperature range in which changes in physical properties are observed after annealing.

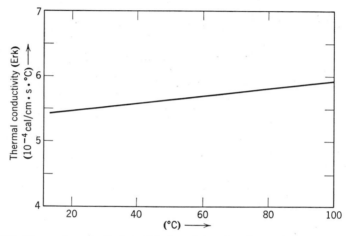

Fig. V-17. Thermal conductivity of bisphenol A polycarbonate versus temperature.

The mechanical and thermal properties of bisphenol A polycarbonate parts can be modified by reinforcing with fiber glass. It is necessary to select a glass with low alkali content in order to avoid degradation of the polycarbonate at elevated temperatures in the presence of moisture and to improve the bond between the glass and the polyester with a special sizing of the fibers (5).

The reinforcing action of the fiber glass considerably increases the tensile strength and the flexural modulus of the parts. Notched impact strength is somewhat reduced but, on the other hand, lacks the tendency to decrease upon heat aging or boiling in water which is characteristic of unfilled specimens of greater thickness (5). Reduced water absorption, higher heat distortion temperatures, and considerably lower coefficients of thermal expansion are other advantages of reinforced parts (5,56).

An investigation of the mechanical properties of polycarbonates under low-frequency dynamic loads over a range of temperatures furnishes

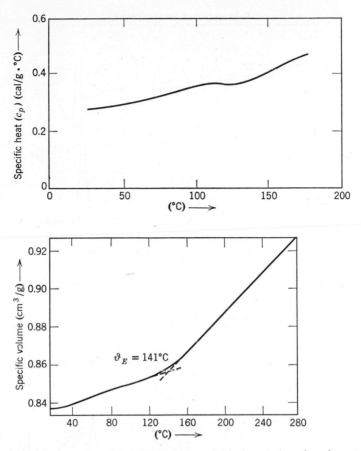

Fig. V-18. Specific heat and specific volume of bisphenol A polycarbonate versus temperature.

evidence regarding molecular motion within the solid material as well as with respect to application technology both from the processor's and the user's point of view. Illers and Breuer (57) used a specially designed recording torsion pendulum to determine the real (G') and the imaginary (G'') portions of the complex dynamic shear modulus and the mechanical damping factor (tan δ) of strip samples of two polycarbonates based on bisphenol A and 1,5-naphthylene-di-(β-hydroxyethyl ether), respectively. Measurements were carried out at an oscillating frequency of 1 cps over the entire temperature range from —180 to +180°C. Figure V-19 contains the plots of G' and tan δ versus temperature for both polycarbonates.

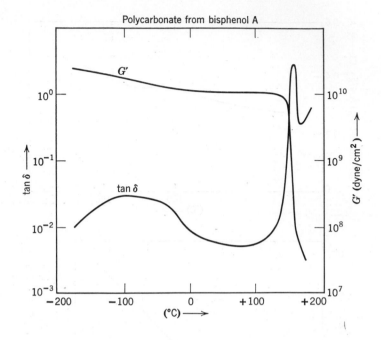

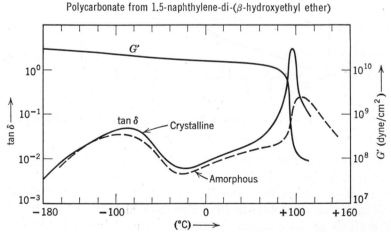

Fig. V-19. Shear modulus G' and damping factor tan δ versus temperature of bisphenol A polycarbonate and 1,5-naphthylene-di-(β-hydroxyethyl ether) polycarbonate (measured at 1 cps).

In the case of bisphenol A polycarbonate the damping factor (tan δ) curve shows a definite narrow peak at 155°C, which corresponds to the change in molecular mobility associated with the second-order transition temperature (149°C). The peak value is approximately tan $\delta = 3$. At the same temperature the shear modulus G', up to that point in the order of 10^{10} dyne/cm², drops off rapidly to very low values. This behavior is similar to that of largely amorphous polymers, such as polystyrene and polyvinyl acetate.

At —97°C the tan δ curve shows a wide and not very pronounced maximum which must be attributed to an overlapping of two relaxation processes. This maximum points out that small parts of the macromolecule retain some mobility down to very low temperatures, thus explaining the extraordinary toughness of this polymer in the low temperature range. In other words, localized stress concentrations developing under external mechanical loads can be absorbed by redistributions in the molecular range down to very low temperatures, thus preventing brittle failure.

The aliphatic components of the 1,5-naphthylene-di-(β-hydroxyethyl ether) polycarbonate molecule are responsible for increased mobility of the macromolecule, thereby increasing its tendency to crystallize. At 150°C it takes only 24 hours to grow crystallites larger than the wavelength of visible light in previously highly amorphous samples.

On amorphous samples the main peak of the tan δ versus temperature curve and the rapid drop in G' values of this aliphatic-aromatic polycarbonate are found at about 98°C. Its second-order transition temperature is about 50°C lower than that of bisphenol A polycarbonate.

For an amorphous sample the maximum tan δ is about 3. Crystallization of the sample shifts the peak to a temperature about 10°C higher, causes it to take on an asymmetrical shape, and reduces the maximum tan δ value by about one order of magnitude.

At the low end of the temperature range the tan δ peak is found near —88°C; crystallinity appears to have little effect on it.

The fact that G', G'', and tan δ, which described the viscoelastic properties of the material, show a change with time at a temperature as low as 100°C indicates that internal stresses set up in making and preparing the samples will with time be reduced even at a temperature 50°C below the second-order transition temperature (57). Reding, Faucher, and Whitman (58), in their investigations of polycarbonates based on bisphenol A, 4,4'-dihydroxy-3,3'-dimethyl-diphenyl-2,2-propane, and 4,4'-dihydroxy-triphenyl-2,2,2-ethane, also found two peaks in the curves of mechanical loss factor (tan δ) versus temperature; their data were measured at frequencies between 0.5 and 1.2 cps, with temperatures ranging from -170 to $+240°$C. One peak is reported below $-100°$C, the other one near the second-order transition temperature of the respective polymer. The authors attribute the low temperature maximum to the mobility of the carbonate groups and the one close to the second-order transition temperature to the mobility of the phenyl groups in the macromolecule.

Deviating in its behavior from the above materials, the 4,4'-dihydroxy-3,3',5,5'-tetrachloro-diphenyl-2,2-propane   (tetrachloro-bisphenol   A) polycarbonate shows a peak in the tan δ versus temperature curve at $+80°$C in addition to the one in the area of the second-order transition temperature.

The mechanical properties of aromatic polycarbonate film are influenced primarily by manufacturing method, molecular weight, molecular weight distribution, crystallinity, and orientation. Film made from bisphenol A polycarbonates with molecular weights M_w between 32,000 and 35,000—materials commonly sold for injection-molding applications—do not display optimum mechanical properties.

Higher molecular weight polycarbonates are therefore used for blown or flat-die extruded film. Films of exceptionally high quality with regard to dimensional stability, absence of surface imperfections, optical clarity, freedom from swell particles, absence of internal stresses, and mechanical strength are obtained from bisphenol A polycarbonates with molecular weights M_w of 85,000 or higher by the solvent casting process. Films ranging in thickness from a few to about 300 μ can be produced on conventional drum- or belt-type casting machines by evaporating the solvent from polycarbonate solutions containing up to 25% solids in a suitable solvent, e.g., methylene chloride.

As it is intended to produce a highly amorphous, optically clear, and colorless film, the attainable thickness is limited by the tendency of thicker films to develop turbidity due to crystal formation (section V, 5). The critical film thickness where this turbidity first starts to occur varies between 150 and 300 μ, depending upon the process employed and the average molecular weight and molecular weight distribution of the polymer used.

Higher solvent removal rates and increasing average molecular weights of the raw material tend to move the critical film thickness toward higher values. Films thicker than 300 μ have been cast successfully without crystal formation from bisphenol A polycarbonate copolymers with reduced crystallization tendency (section V, 5).

The mechanical properties of cast film are adversely affected by an extremely wide molecular weight distribution function. Film made, for example, from a bisphenol A polycarbonate with a broad distribution curve with two peaks was found to have a crackling "feel," somewhat similar to thin aluminum foil, and comparatively poor mechanical properties (1).

Since crystallization in solid bisphenol A polycarbonate is strongly inhibited (section V, 5), nonstretched as well as stretch-oriented amorphous film retains its physical characteristics for all practical purposes indefinitely at room temperature. Similar to injection-molded parts, these

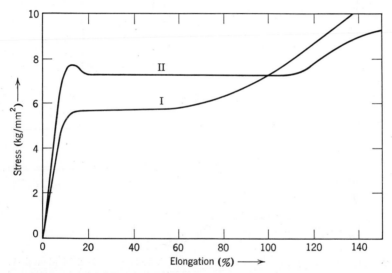

Fig. V-20. Stress-strain diagram of highly amorphous (I) and a crystallized (II) bisphenol A polycarbonate film (film thickness: I–0.02 mm; II–0.07 mm).

films increase slightly in their rigidity at temperatures around 100°C but do not lose any of their favorable mechanical properties. Bisphenol A polycarbonate film may thus find application in the highly amorphous, the amorphous and stretch-oriented, the crystallized, and the crystallized and oriented forms. Orientation by stretching can be in one direction or in two directions perpendicular to each other. A wide selection of mechanical properties is thus available to answer specific application requirements.

Using a bisphenol A polycarbonate with an average molecular weight of $M_w = 86{,}000$, Hofmeier (59) studied the mechanical properties of solvent cast film as a function of crystallinity and orientation. Up to about 5 kg/mm² the stress-strain diagram of a highly amorphous film (Fig. V-20) shows essentially a straight-line relationship. At that point the stretching region begins where orientation of the macromolecules sets in and is accompanied by an increase of tenacity. Failure occurs at a stress

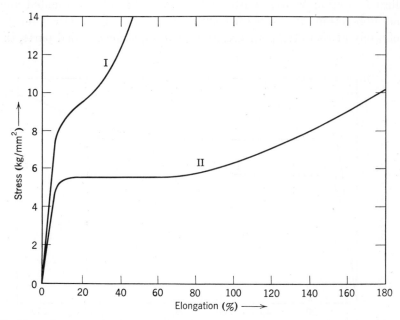

Fig. V-21. Stress-strain diagram of a one-directionally stretched bisphenol A poly-carbonate film obtained on samples cut parallel (I) and perpendicular (II) to the direction of orientation by stretching (draw ratio 3·5:1).

of about 10 kg/mm² (calculated on the original cross-sectional area) and about 120% elongation.

The curve for the crystallized film distinctly shows the linear range extended to about 7 kg/mm². In the stretched region that follows the strength increase associated with the oriented state appears suddenly at a high elongation, where a break shows in the stress-strain curve. The specimen fails at approximately 9 kg/mm², having undergone an elongation of 150%. The fact that the ultimate tensile strength of this film at room temperature seems to be lower than that of the amorphous film is

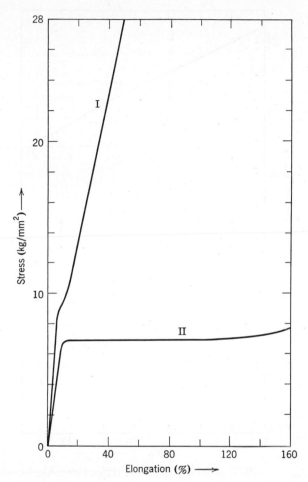

Fig. V-22. Stress-strain diagram of a one-directionally stretched crystallized bisphenol A polycarbonate film obtained on samples cut parallel (I) and perpendicular (II) to the direction of orientation by stretching (thickness 0.02 mm).

most likely due to microscopic flaws in the film caused by the stretching process carried out under unfavorable conditions.

If an amorphous film is stretched in one direction only, the stress-strain curve of a sample cut perpendicular to the direction of orientation by stretching remains essentially unaffected (Fig. V-21). In the direction of orientation by stretching the linear portion of the stress-strain curve is extended to about 8 kg/mm^2 and shows a substantial increase in the

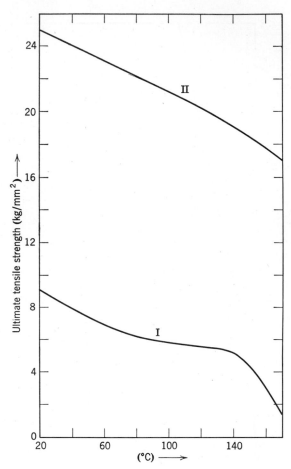

Fig. V-23. Ultimate tensile strength of amorphous (I) and stretch-oriented and crystallized (II) bisphenol A polycarbonate film versus temperature.

modulus of elasticity. The nonlinear portion of the curve is similar to that of the nonstretched sample, except for a greater slope. In the direction of orientation by stretching failure occurs at approximately 14 kg/mm², corresponding to an elongation of 45%.

With these samples the nonlinear portion of the stress-strain curve, starting at about 8 kg/mm², is very steep. The ultimate tensile strength of this film is 28 kg/mm² with an elongation of 55%.

Particularly desirable, from an application point of view, are the elevated temperature properties of bisphenol A polycarbonate film. According to Figure V-23, unstretched amorphous film loses only 40% of its room-temperature ultimate tensile strength when heated to 140°C. About the second-order transition temperature softening of the film causes a rapid deterioration of the ultimate tensile strength with increasing temperature.

In a stretch-oriented and crystallized film the ultimate tensile strength does not show this rapid drop above the second-order transition temperature. At 140°C almost 80% of the room-temperature tensile strength is still available, and even at temperatures in excess of 220°C crystallized and stretched film suffers only little plastic deformation under a load of 1 kg/mm².

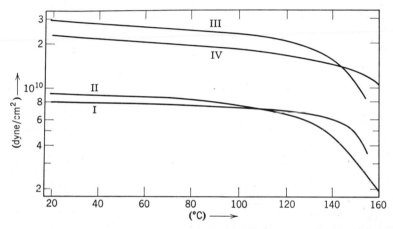

Fig. V-24. Shear modulus versus temperature of amorphous (I), crystallized (II), stretch-oriented amorphous (III), and stretch-oriented and crystallized (IV) bisphenol A polycarbonate film.

Measurements of the shear modulus for various conditions of crystallinity, orientation, and temperature (Fig. V-24) confirm, in the case of amorphous and crystallized film, the previously reported (Fig. V-19) value of 10^{10} dyne/cm², dropping off near the second-order transition temperature.

Orientation by stretching causes the shear modulus to go up, and, although in a stretch-oriented amorphous film a rapid decrease of the shear modulus is still observed near the second-order transition temperature, high shear modulus values (59) are retained at 160°C in a stretch-oriented and crystallized film.

Only exploratory data, correlating the mechanical properties of film made from aromatic polycarbonates with the nature of the dihydroxy compounds used in their preparation (2) (Table V-16), have been published.

TABLE V-16

Mechanical Properties of Solvent Cast Film Made from Various Aromatic Polycarbonates

Polycarbonate from	Orientation	Tensile strength [kg/cm^2]	Elonga- tion [%]	Impact strength [cm·kg/cm^3] (I.G. method)	Flexing cycles
4,4'-Dihydroxy-diphenyl					
-1,1-ethane	Nonstretched	750	167	1013	>10,000
-1,1-isobutane	Nonstretched	775	147	300	>10,000
-2,2-propane	Nonstretched	820	180	900	>10,000
	draw ratio 1:2	1400 1700*	32–40	. . .	>10,000
	1:4.7 stretched crystallized	2150*	14	425	>10,000
	1:11 stretched	3500*	20	320	>10,000
	Blown foil	890	155	700	>10,000
-2,2-butane	Nonstretched	725	70	363	5,800
-2,2-pentane	Nonstretched	665	66	703	900
4,4'-Dihydroxy-triphenyl- 2,2,2-ethane	Nonstretched	824	55	172	1,000
4,4'-Dihydroxy-diphenyl					
-1,1-cyclohexane	Nonstretched	814	56	169	5,000
-1,1-cyclopentane	Nonstretched	708	119	552	>10,000
4,4'-Dihydroxy-3,3- dichloro-diphenyl- propane	Nonstretched	995	19	65	>10,000
4,4'-Dihydroxy-3,3',5,5'- tetrachloro-diphenyl- 2,2-propane	Nonstretched	1154	10	33	3,000
4,4'-Dihydroxy-3,3',5,5'- tetrabromo-diphenyl- 2,2-propane	Nonstretched	1112	8	36	1,000

* In the direction of stretching.

The measurements carried out on film samples 50 to 60 μ thick indicated that all the aromatic polycarbonates based on 4,4'-dihydroxy-diphenyl methane derivatives that were investigated produced films with similar mechanical properties.

Only scant information is available on the mechanical properties of polycarbonate fibers. Textile and commercial applications will be limited to fibers both stretched and crystallized. Such fibers may attain tenacities of more than 4 g/denier at about 30% elongation (37).

7. ELECTRICAL PROPERTIES OF AROMATIC POLYCARBONATES

The favorable electrical properties of aromatic polycarbonates were recognized at an early date (60). Intelligent application of polycarbonates in the electrical industry for injection-molded parts, film, fibers, coatings, etc., requires a knowledge of the electrical properties, such as dielectric constant, dielectric loss angle, insulation resistance, and tracking resistance, as well as how these properties are affected by the shape, size, moisture content, and aging history of the parts and by environmental conditions, particularly humidity and temperature.

In addition, dielectric loss measurements as a function of temperature and frequency can furnish information on molecular mobility within the solid material.

The electrical properties, particularly of the bisphenol A polycarbonate, have been the subject of many investigations predominantly in the United States and Germany (1 through 5, 29, 39, 47, 59 through 63, 65 through 70). Other aromatic polycarbonates have been investigated only in an exploratory fashion.

Table V-17 summarizes the electrical properties of commercial bisphenol A polycarbonates as determined on injection-molded parts in accordance with United States (5,29,47) in German (72) standard methods.

The electrical properties of highly amorphous commercial bisphenol A polycarbonate film, both stretched and nonstretched, are given in Table V-18 (69).

Bisphenol A polycarbonate, in accordance with its largely nonpolar character, displays favorable electrical properties at room temperature, particularly along the lines of high insulating value and low dielectric loss at frequencies between 50 cps and 1 mc/sec. Water absorption as a result of immersion or exposure to more or less humid air changes the electrical properties very little because of the low moisture pickup of the polymer. Molecular weight has essentially no effect on electrical properties. Curves of the dielectric constant and dissipation factor versus frequency are shown in Figure V-25 (p. 161) (5,29,39).

The dielectric constant shows no significant change between 10 and 10^8 cps. The dissipation factor tan δ increases with frequency until it reaches a flat-topped maximum at 10^7 cps, then decreases again with a further increase in frequency.

Since much of the equipment utilizing polycarbonate as a dielectric is called upon to perform at elevated temperatures, the variations of the

TABLE V-17. Electrical Properties of Injection-Molded Bisphenol A Polycarbonate

Property	Method	Value	Property	Test method ASTM	Value
Dielectric strength [kv/cm] (50 cps, 0.5 kv/sec)	VDE 0303, section 2 DIN 53,481 circular disk 95-mm diameter, 1 mm thick		Dielectric strength short time [V/mil] (23°C)	D149	
dry		270	1.5 mils		3190
stored 4 days at 80% relative humidity		260	3.0 mils		3080
24-hour water immersion		260	4.7 mils		2560
Surface resistivity [Ohm]	VDE 0303, section 3 DIN 53,482 standard test bar 120 × 15 × 4 mm		23.0 mils		1130
dry		$>10^{15}$	125.0 mils		400
stored 4 days at 80% relative humidity		$>10^{15}$	Volume resistivity [Ohm·cm] (23°C)	. . .	$2.1 \cdot 10^{16}$
24-hour water immersion		$>10^{15}$	Arc resistance	D495	
Volume resistivity [Ohm·cm]	VDE 0303, section 3 DIN 53,482 circular disk 95-mm diameter, 1 mm thick		Stainless steel strip electrodes		10–11 sec
dry		$>10^{17}$	Tungsten electrodes		120 sec
stored 4 days at 80% relative humidity		$>10^{16}$	Dielectric constant (23°C)	D150	
24-hour water immersion		$>10^{16}$	60 cycles		3.17
Dielectric constant, dry	VDE 0303, section 4 DIN 53,483 circular disk 80-mm diameter		10^6 cycles		2.96
			10^{10} cycles		2.74
			Power factor (23°C)	D150	
			60 cycles		0.0009
			10^6 cycles		0.010
			10^{10} cycles		0.005

at 50 cps		3.0
at 800 cps		2.95
at 1 mc/sec		2.90
Dissipation factor, tan δ, dry	VDE 0303, section 4 DIN 53,483 circular disk 95- and 30-mm diameter, 1 mm thick	
at 50 cps		0.0007
at 800 cps		0.0013
at 1 mc/sec		0.0110
Tracking resistance	VDE 0303, section 1 DIN-Entwurf 53,480 (January 1959) disk, 20 × 15 mm	
test solution A		T_2–T_3
test solution F		T_4–T_5
Tracking resistance	VDE 0303, section 1 DIN-Entwurf 53,480 (December 1961) circular disk 118-mm diameter, 4 mm thick	
test method A		A1
test solution A		
test method B		B360
test solution F		
Water absorption [mg] 4 days immersion test	DIN 53,472 disk 50 × 50 × 1 mm	10

TABLE V-18

Electrical Properties of Highly Amorphous Solvent Cast Bisphenol
A Polycarbonate Film in the Stretch-Oriented and Nonstretch-Oriented State

Property	Method	Highly amorphous nonstretch-oriented	Highly amorphous stretch-oriented
Dielectric strength [kv/mm] (50 cps, 0.5 kv/sec)	VDE 0303, section 2 DIN 53,481		
sample thickness 0.04–0.2 mm stored 4 days at 80% relative humidity		155	146
Surface resistivity [Ohm] stored 4 days at 80% relative humidity	VDE 0303, section 3 DIN 53,482	10^{13}	10^{13}
Volume resistivity [Ohm·cm]	VDE 0303, section 3 DIN 53,482		
dry		10^{17}	10^{17}
stored 4 days at 80% relative humidity		4×10^{16}	
24-hour water immersion		3×10^{16}	8×10^{15}
Dielectric constant, dry	VDE 0303, section 4 DIN 53,483		
at 50 cps		3.1	3.0
at 800 cps		3.0	2.9
at 1 mc/sec		2.9	2.9
Dissipation factor, tan δ, dry	VDE 0303, section 4 DIN 53,483		
at 50 cps		0.0025	0.0009
at 800 cps		0.0020	0.0011
at 1 mc/sec		0.0087	0.0098
Water absorption [%] 24-hr immersion at 20°C		0.5	0.5

dielectric values with temperature, particularly the dissipation factor, are of great practical importance. They are also of scientific interest, since they supply detailed evidence with respect to molecular mobility phenomena within the solid material.

A plot of the dissipation factor tan δ versus temperature measured on bisphenol A polycarbonate at 20 kc/sec over a range from —120 to +190°C is shown in Figure V-26 (70).

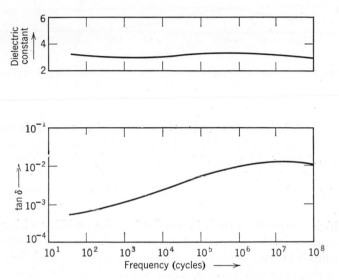

Fig. V-25. Dielectric constant and dissipation factor of bisphenol A polycarbonate versus frequency, measured at 22°C and 50% relative humidity.

The curve, which is in agreement with experimental results reported by Krum, Müller, and Huff (66,67,68), displays a high as well as a low temperature peak, the same as the temperature function of the mechanical damping factor (section V, 6).

Both peaks are shifted toward higher temperatures by an increase in frequency. A summary of the temperatures associated with the tan δ peaks at various frequencies is given in Table V-19. The corresponding data for the mechanical loss factor at a frequency of 1 cps have been included in the table for the purpose of comparison.

The low-temperature peak is attributed to the mobility of the CO-group (carbonyl dipole) in the alternating electric field. This assumption is indicated by a comparison of the tan δ low-temperature peaks of poly-

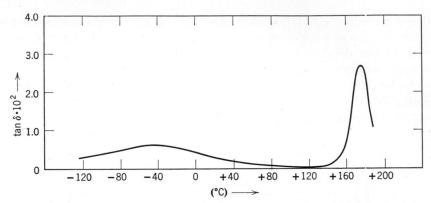

Fig. V-26. Dissipation factor versus temperature of bisphenol A polycarbonate at 20 kc/sec.

ethyleneterephthalate (66) and polyesters made from bisphenol A with sebacic acid, isophthalic acid, and terephthalic acid, respectively, (70), with those determined for the bisphenol A polycarbonate. For all of these polymers a direct relationship can be shown between the low-temperature peak heights of the tan δ plot and the number of CO-groups per unit volume.

The high-temperature peak is ascribed to the mobility of larger molecules segments in the alternating electric field. There is a corresponding relationship between the high-temperature tan δ peaks and the number of aromatic rings per unit volume, when bisphenol A polycarbonate is com-

TABLE V-19

Locations of the Tan δ Peaks as a Function of
Frequency for Bisphenol A Polycarbonate

Measuring frequency [cps]	Low temperature peak at [°C], approx.	High temperature peak at [°C], approx.	Reference
1	−97	155	(57)
10^3	−80	175	(66)
10^4	−60	180	(66)
$2 \cdot 10^4$	−40	174	(70)
10^5	−30	190	(66)
$3.16 \cdot 10^5$	−20	. . .	(66)

pared with polyethyleneterephthalate (66) and polyesters made from bisphenol A with sebacic acid, isophthalic acid, or terephthalic acid (70). The phenomena of molecular mobility, which are responsible for the high-temperature peaks in the tan δ-temperature curves, are the same that cause various physical properties to change at the second-order transition temperature (section V, 2).

Evidence concerning the activation energies associated with molecular mobility in the alternating electric field is contained in the temperature shifts of the tan δ peaks with changes in measuring frequency. For the

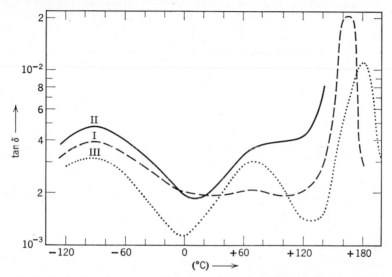

Fig. V-27. Dissipation factor tan δ versus temperature of nonstretched (I), stretch-oriented (II) and stretch-oriented and crystallized (III) bisphenol A polycarbonate film (measured at 1 kc/sec).

relaxation processes corresponding to the low-temperature tan δ maxima observed in bisphenol A polycarbonates activation energies of about 7 to 9 kcal/mole were calculated by Krum, Müller, and Huff (66,67,68) as well as by Michailov and Eidelnant (70); for the relaxation processes associated with the high temperature peaks these authors report activation energies between about 115 and 137 kcal/mole.

Crystallinity and orientation both have an effect on the curves of dielectric values versus temperature. Figure V-27 illustrates this effect by combining the schematic tan δ versus temperature curves of solvent cast bisphenol A polycarbonate film in the nonstretched, highly amorphous (I), the stretch-oriented, highly amorphous (II), and the stretch-oriented and crystallized (III) condition, measured at a frequency of 1 kc/sec (59).

Orientation of the macromolecules causes a shift of the high-temperature peak toward lower temperatures. Also, a new peak appears at about +80°C (66,67,68). The position of this peak changes as a function of frequency. As the measuring frequency is increased, it tends to move upward on the temperature scale, flattening out at the same time.

Crystallization reduces the dielectric loss. Also, the high-temperature peak in the tan δ versus temperature curve is displaced toward higher temperatures (66,68,70). The activation energy of the relaxation proc-

TABLE V-20

Electrical Properties of Aromatic Polycarbonates

Polycarbonate based on	tan δ ·10^{-4} 1000 cps 25°C	Dielectric constant 1000 cps 25°C	tan δ ·10^{-4} 1000 cps 100°C	Dielectric constant 1000 cps 100°C
4,4'-Dihydroxy-diphenyl				
-1,1-ethane	4.9	2.9	4.9	2.9
-1,1-butane	5.2	3.3	5.2	3.3
-1,1-isobutane	5.2	2.4	5.2	2.4
-1,1-cyclopentane	5.0	2.9	5.0	2.9
-1,1-cyclohexane	11.2	3.0	11.2	3.0
-2,2-propane	4.9	2.8	4.9	2.8
-2,2-butane	4.5	3.1	4.5	3.1
-2,2-pentane	4.2	2.3	4.2	2.3
4,4'-Dihydroxy-triphenyl-2,2,2- ethane	5.0	3.3	5.0	3.3
4,4'-Dihydroxy -3,3'-dimethyl-diphenyl- 1,1-ethane	9.9	3.4	90.0	3.6
-3,3'-dimethyl-diphenyl- 2,2-propane	20.4	2.5	40.0	2.6
-3,3'-dichloro-diphenyl- 2,2-propane	11.5	3.3	16.0	3.6
-3,3',5,5'-tetrachloro- diphenyl-2,2-propane	10.0	3.0	37.0	3.0
-3,3',5,5'-tetrachloro- diphenyl-1,1-cyclohexane	5.0	2.6	40.0	2.6
-3,3',5,5'-tetrabromo- diphenyl-2,2-propane	20.0	2.7	38.0	2.7

esses associated with the low-temperature peak increases from 9 to about 13 kcal/mol as a result of crystallization.

In the oriented and crystallized condition a general reduction of the dielectric losses over the entire temperature range is evident. The high-temperature peak is moved up about 15 to 20°C. The orientation peak separates itself from the high-temperature peak and becomes more pronounced.

From a practical point of view the low dielectric loss, or dissipation factor, in alternating electric fields at temperatures up to 140°C makes bisphenol A polycarbonates particularly valuable to the electrical industry. The high-temperature stability and excellent aging characteristics of the polymer allow full advantage to be taken of this quality. Other aromatic polycarbonates display similar features as shown in Table V-20 (2).

Many aromatic polycarbonates based on 4,4'-dihydroxy-diphenyl methane derivatives with substitutions on the aromatic rings exhibit a steady increase in the dielectric losses as the temperature rises above room temperature, and their tan δ versus temperature functions do not pass through a maximum. A distinct peak in the tan δ versus temperature curve near the second-order transition temperature is always found, however, in aromatic polycarbonates based on 4,4'-dihydroxy-diphenyl methane derivatives not substituted on the aromatic group.

8. REFRACTIVE INDEX AND LIGHT TRANSMITTANCE OF AROMATIC POLYCARBONATES

Following thermoplastic processing or casting from solution, most of the aromatic polycarbonates based on dihydroxy-diphenyl methane derivatives are obtained as clear transparent parts, unless some special effort has been made to promote crystallinity (section V, 5). Quantitative data on light transmittance in the visible and ultraviolet range and the refractive index are important for many commercial applications, such as in the lighting and optical industries as well as in the packaging field. In the infrared range characteristic absorption spectra are observed, which may be used to identify the different aromatic polycarbonates (section V, 12).

Table V-21 for a number of aromatic polycarbonates shows the refractive indices for the D-line of the sodium spectrum at 25°C (1,2).

The refractive index ranges from 1.56 to 1.65 covered all the aromatic polycarbonates investigated.

TABLE V-21

Refractive Indices of Aromatic Polycarbonates

Polycarbonate based on	Refractive index n_D (25°C)
4,4'-Dihydroxy-diphenyl-1,1-ethane	1.5937
"　　　"　　　"　　-1,1-butane	1.5792
"　　　"　　　"　　-1,1-isobutane	1.5702
"　　　"　　　"　　-1,1-cyclopentane	1.5993
"　　　"　　　"　　-1,1-cyclohexane	1.5900
"　　　"　　　"　　-2,2-propane	1 5850
"　　　"　　　"　　-2,2-butane	1.5827
"　　　"　　　"　　-2,2-pentane	1.5745
"　　　"　　　"　　-2,2-(4-methyl pentane)	1.5671
"　　　"　　　"　　-4,4-heptane	1.5602
"　　　"　　-triphenyl-2,2,2-ethane	1.6130
"　　　"　　-triphenyl methane	1.6539
"　　　"　　-3,3'-dichloro-diphenyl-2,2-propane	1.5900
"　　　"　　-3,3',5,5'-tetrachloro-diphenyl-2,2-propane	1.6056
"　　　"　　-3,3',5,5'-tetrabromo-diphenyl-2,2-propane	1.6147
"　　　"　　-3,3',5,5'-tetrachloro-diphenyl-1,1-cyclohexane	1.5858
"　　　"　　-3,3'-dimethyl-diphenyl-2,2-propane	1.5783

Figure V-28 shows the light transmittance curve in the visible and ultraviolet range for bisphenol A polycarbonate (39).

For this polycarbonate the light transmittance in the visible spectrum of a 100-μ solvent cast film varies between 85 and 90%. In the ultraviolet range transmittance drops off rapidly.

At the present time it is not possible to obtain completely colorless parts from commercial bisphenol A polycarbonates. As sections increase in thickness, a yellowish color becomes apparent. This color, however, is not an inherent quality of the material but is the result rather of impurities introduced with the intermediates, manufacturing methods, and, to some extent, the processing of the material. Further development of all the processes involved to the point at which essentially colorless polycarbonates will be available is definitely within the realm of possibility.

Figures V-29 through V-41 show the infrared absorption spectra of a series of aromatic polycarbonates (3, 71). The curves in Figure V-29 and V-41 were determined on KBr-molded specimens (0.5% b.w.), the others on film samples.

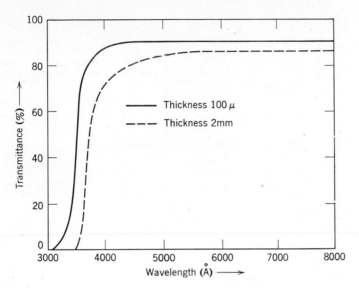

Fig. V-28. Light transmittance of bisphenol A polycarbonate.

A number of characteristic bands reoccur in the infrared absorption spectra of all the polycarbonates that were investigated; these can be assigned to the following vibrations (with deviations found only in the case of chlorine-substituted ring systems):

at   3.3 μ: C—H stretching vibration of the aromatic rings
about   5.65 μ: C=O stretching vibration of the carbonate group
          8.1 μ: ⎫
          8.4 μ: ⎬ asymmetrical O—C—O stretching vibration of the carbonate group
          8.6 μ: ⎭
at   9.9 μ: symmetrical O—C—O stretching vibration of the carbonate group
at   13 μ: "out of plane" vibrations of the carbonate group (not very intense).

Different types of substitution on the aromatic rings can be identified on the basis of the "out of plane" deformations of the ring's C-H groups (the 1,4-substitution, for example, produces a strong band close to 12.0 μ and a weak band around 13.0 μ). In a similar manner the different substitutions give rise to distinct band locations between 6.2 and 6.8 μ for the C=C vibrations, and changes in the alkyl groups occupying the middle

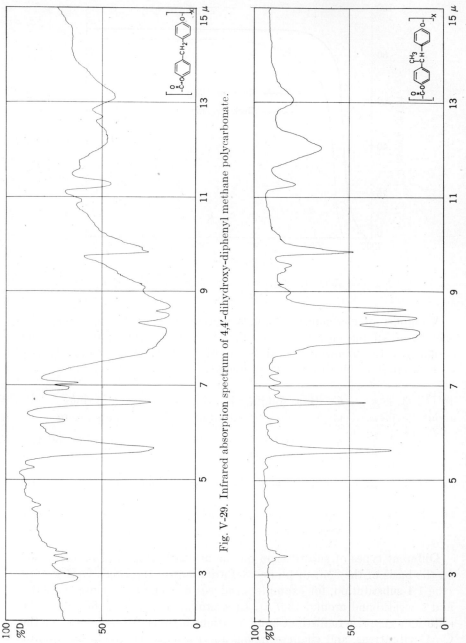

Fig. V-29. Infrared absorption spectrum of 4,4'-dihydroxy-diphenyl methane polycarbonate.

Fig. V-30. Infrared absorption spectrum of 4,4'-dihydroxy-diphenyl-1,1-ethane polycarbonate.

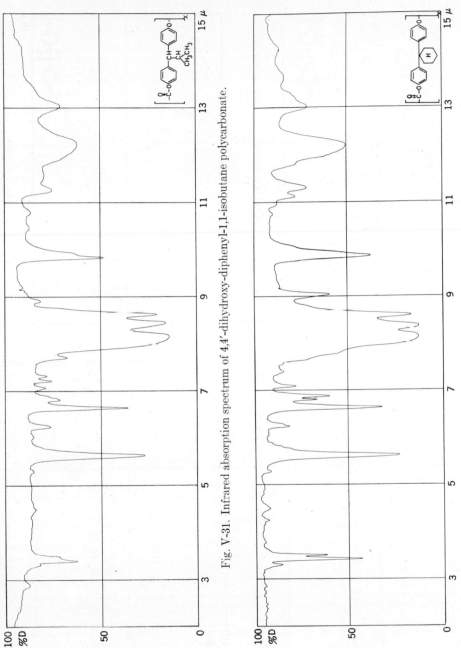

Fig. V-31. Infrared absorption spectrum of 4,4'-dihydroxy-diphenyl-1,1-isobutane polycarbonate.

Fig. V-32. Infrared absorption spectrum of 4,4'-dihydroxy-diphenyl-1,1-cyclohexane polycarbonate.

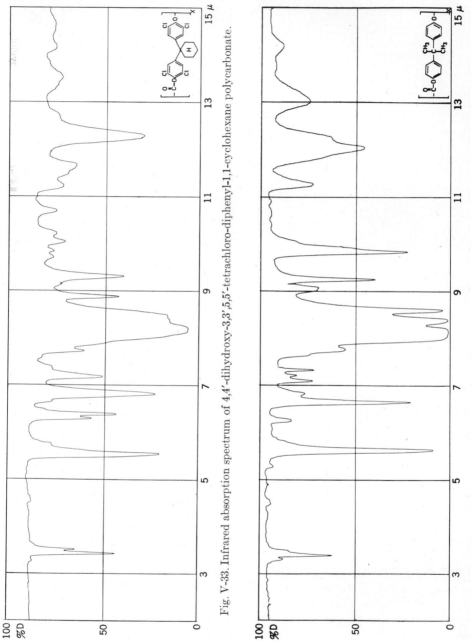

Fig. V-33. Infrared absorption spectrum of 4,4'-dihydroxy-3,3',5,5'-tetrachloro-diphenyl-1,1-cyclohexane polycarbonate.

Fig. V-34. Infrared absorption spectrum of 4,4'-dihydroxy-diphenyl-2,2-propane (bis-phenol A) polycarbonate.

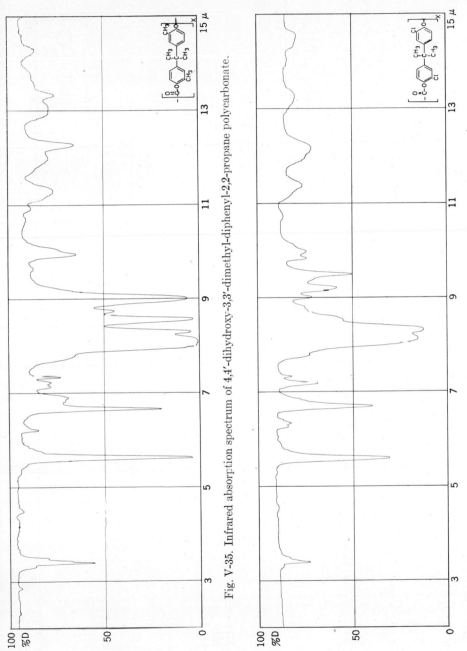

Fig. V-35. Infrared absorption spectrum of 4,4'-dihydroxy-3,3'-dimethyl-diphenyl-2,2-propane polycarbonate.

Fig. V-36. Infrared absorption spectrum of 4,4'-dihydroxy-3,3'-dichloro-diphenyl-2,2-propane polycarbonate.

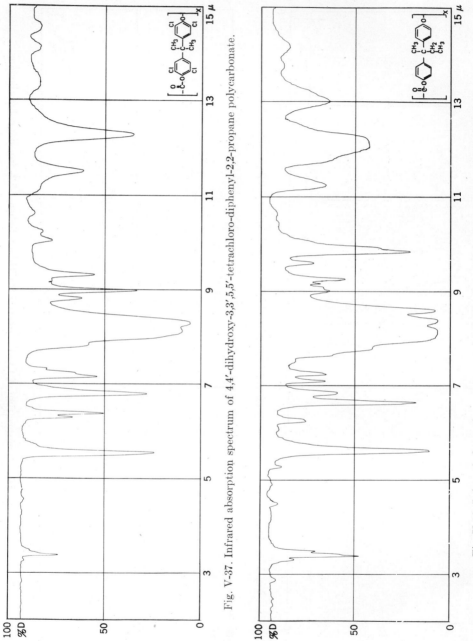

Fig. V-37. Infrared absorption spectrum of 4,4'-dihydroxy-3,3',5,5'-tetrachloro-diphenyl-2,2-propane polycarbonate.

Fig. V-38. Infrared absorption spectrum of 4,4'-dihydroxy-diphenyl-2,2-butane polycarbonate.

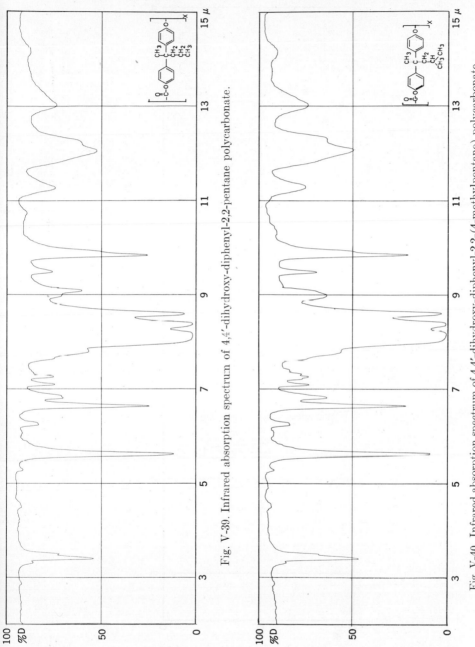

Fig. V-39. Infrared absorption spectrum of 4,4'-dihydroxy-diphenyl-2,2-pentane polycarbonate.

Fig. V-40. Infrared absorption spectrum of 4,4'-dihydroxy-diphenyl-2,2-(4-methylpentane) polycarbonate.

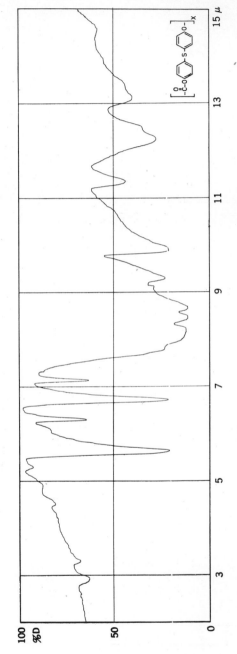

Fig. V-41. Infrared absorption spectrum of 4,4'-dihydroxy-diphenyl sulfide polycarbonate.

position are reflected in the IR absorption spectra by a change-in-band intensity in the range of the aliphatic C—H bond frequency (3.4 — 3.55μ).A

$$\begin{array}{c} \mathrm{C} \\ {\diagup} \quad {\diagdown} \\ \mathrm{CH_3} \quad \mathrm{CH_3} \end{array}$$

arrangement causes a split of the CH$_3$ deformation into two bands (7.2 and 7.35 μ) and the appearance of two new bands at 9.3 and 12.3 μ.

These general relationships are disturbed if the aromatic ring systems are repeatedly substituted by halogen atoms, as in the case of the 4,4'-dihydroxy-3,3',5,5'-tetrachloro-diphenyl-2,2-propane polycarbonate (Fig. V-37). The C=O band undergoes a shift toward shorter wavelengths and is found at 5.55 μ, whereas the bands resulting from the asymmetric O—C—O vibration are changed in their location and shape (there are only two strong bands at 8.13 and 8.3 μ left). At the same time the band of the symmetrical O—C—O-vibration is displaced in the direction of longer wavelengths. The strong band at 12.3 μ can probably be allocated to the C—Cl bond vibration, whereas the "out of plane" deformation of the two hydrogen atoms remaining attached to the benzene ring is responsible for the band at 11.55 μ.

Table V-22 summarizes the most important infrared absorption bands of these aromatic polycarbonates; it will be recognized that the bands attributable to the carbonate group vibrations are sufficiently fixed in their position to permit the identification of aromatic polycarbonates.

9. WATER ABSORPTION, WATER VAPOR PERMEABILITY, AND GAS PERMEABILITY OF AROMATIC POLYCARBONATES

As a result of their largely nonpolar character, the aromatic polycarbonates will absorb only small amounts of moisture when exposed to water or water vapor.

The equilibrium moisture content will depend on the chemical nature of the polycarbonate, its crystallinity and orientation, the temperature of the system, and, if the exposure is to a vapor mixture, the partial pressure of the water vapor. Bisphenol A polycarbonate immersed in water at 25°C will absorb a maximum of 0.36% water. Figure V-42 shows the moisture pick-up of 15 $\times$ 4 $\times$ 120 mm injection-molded samples at 25°C in contact with water and with air of 60% relative humidity; long periods of time are required to reach equilibrium (39).

TABLE V-22. Locations of the Most Important Absorption Bands of Aromatic Polycarbonates

No.	Fig. No.	Polycarbonate based on	C=O stretching vibration [μ]	Asymmetrical O—C—O stretching vibration [μ]	Symmetrical O—C—O stretching vibration [μ]	Out-of-plane vibration of the carbonate group * [μ]	C—H out-of-plane deformation [μ]	Note
1	V-29	HO—C₆H₄—CH₂—C₆H₄—OH	5.65	8.15 } 8.7 8.50	≈9.9	13.1	12.2	KBr (0.5%)
2	V-30	HO—C₆H₄—CH(CH₃)—C₆H₄—OH	5.63	8.15 } 8.62 8.44	9.85	≈13.0	12.05	Film
3	V-31	HO—C₆H₄—CH(CH(CH₃)CH₃)—C₆H₄—OH	5.63	8.15 } 8.62 8.45	9.83	13.05	≈12.25	Film
4	V-32	HO—C₆H₄—C(CH₂CH₂CH₂)(CH₂CH₂CH₂)—C₆H₄—OH	5.62	8.15 } 8.60 8.37	9.85	13.05	12.25	Film
5	V-33	(Cl)₂HO—C₆H₂—C(CH₂CH₂CH₂)(CH₂CH₂CH₂)—C₆H₂(Cl)₂—OH	5.56	8.20 8.45	10.05	…	11.60	Film
6	V-34	HO—C₆H₄—C(CH₃)(CH₃)—C₆H₄—OH	5.63	8.15 } 8.60 8.40	9.85	13.05	12.1	Film

No.	Code	Structure							Medium
7	V-35	(tetramethyl bisphenol A)	5.64	8.10 / 8.30 } 8.57	9.95	≈13.0	11.3 / 12.3		Film
8	V-36	(dichloro bisphenol A)	5.60	8.12 / 8.32	10.0	13.05 (sh)	11.4 / 12.2		Film
9	V-37	(tetrachloro bisphenol A)	5.56	8.13 / 8.32	10.06	…	11.52		Film
10	V-38		5.62	8.15 / 8.40 } 8.60	9.85	13.0	12.2		Film
11	V-39		5.63	8.15 / 8.37 } 8.60	9.85	≈13.0	12.1		Film
12	V-40		5.63	8.15 / 8.40 } 8.60	9.88	13.0	12.1		Film
13	V-41		5.65	8.20 / 8.45 } 8.66	9.9	13.10	12.25		KBr (0.5%)

* A medium strength band, associated with the out-of-plane deformation of the C—H group in the disubstituted ring.

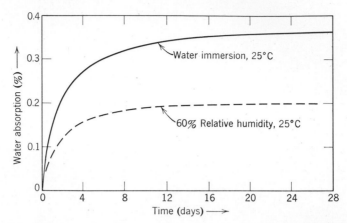

Fig. V-42. Water absorption of bisphenol A polycarbonate at 25°C.

At 60% relative humidity equilibrium is reached at about 0.20% moisture. Very important from the application point of view is the fact that the absorption of this water does not virtually produce any dimensional changes in the specimens. The molecular structure of the highly amorphous solid parts apparently contains sufficient space to accommodate the water.

Water absorption of other aromatic polycarbonates differs little from that of the bisphenol A based material, as illustrated by Table V-23.

The permeability to water vapor of aromatic polycarbonates is strongly dependent upon the thickness of the barrier. Table V-24 presents a summary of data measured on solvent cast film 80 to 100 μ thick at 20°C (2).

TABLE V-23

Water Absorption of Aromatic Polycarbonates at
25°C and 65% Relative Humidity

Polycarbonate based on	Water absorption [%]
4,4′-Dihydroxy-diphenyl-2,2-butane	0.2
" " " -2,2-pentane	0.2
" " " -methyl-isobutyl methane	0.1
" " " -1,1-cyclopentane	0.2
" " " -1,1-cyclohexane	0.2
" " -triphenyl-2,2,2-ethane	0.2

TABLE V-24

Water Vapor Permeability of Aromatic Polycarbonates

Polycarbonate based on	Water vapor permeability $\times 10^8$ at 20°C [g/cm·hr·mm Hg]
4,4'-Dihydroxy-diphenyl-2,2-propane	3.0
" " " -1,1-cyclopentane	1.5
" " " -1,1-cyclohexane	1.0
" " -triphenyl-2,2,2-ethane	2.4
" " -3,3'-dichloro-diphenyl-2,2-propane	0.6
" " -3,3',5,5'-tetrachloro-diphenyl-2,2-propane	2.1
" " -3,3',5,5'-tetrabromo-diphenyl-2,2-propane	2.3
" " -3,3',5,5'-tetrachloro-diphenyl-1,1-cyclohexane	1.1

The variation of water vapor permeability with film thickness is illustrated by the plot in Figure V-43 (39).

Table V-25 contains a summary of data on the permeability of bisphenol A polycarbonate film to various gases; tests were conducted on solvent cast film approximately 50 μ thick at 20°C. The results of the measurements are compiled, using the dimensions cubic centimeters of gas (at standard conditions of 760 mm Hg and 0°C) per second, square centimeter film area, cm film thickness, and cm mercury column absolute gas pressure, which contracts to cm²/sec·cm Hg (72).

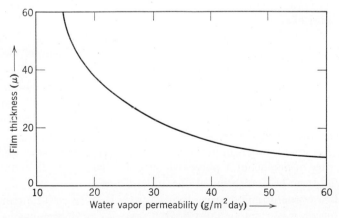

Fig. V-43. Water vapor permeability of bisphenol A polycarbonate film versus film thickness.

TABLE V-25

Gas Permeability of Bisphenol A Polycarbonate

Gas	Permeability [cm²/sec · cm Hg]
Hydrogen	2.62×10^{-9}
Carbon dioxide	1.50×10^{-9}
Oxygen	0.51×10^{-9}
Nitrogen	0.017×10^{-9}
Air	0.097×10^{-9}
Ethylene oxide	0.77×10^{-9}
Methane	4.47×10^{-11}
Ethane	3.82×10^{-12}
Propane	5.48×10^{-12}
Butane	6.96×10^{-13}

No information has become available to date regarding the effects of orientation and crystallinity on the vapor permeability of aromatic poly-carbonate film.

10. AGING AND CHEMICAL RESISTANCE OF BISPHENOL A POLYCARBONATE

The resistance of bisphenol A polycarbonate to environmental factors, such as temperature, water, moisture, air, oxygen, light, acids, alkalies, solvents, and chemicals (64,73,74), is influenced by the crystallinity and orientation as well as by the shape, size, and past history of any given sample. Oriented and crystallized fibers or film, for instance, will stand up successfully to a number of solvents which are capable of dissolving or swelling highly amorphous material.

Internal stresses set up during manufacturing operations or tensile stress may cause stress cracking, especially under the influence of elevated temperature, water, or swelling agents (23,75).

Data presented further on in this section on aging properties and chemical resistance of bisphenol A polycarbonate are true for largely amorphous resin in the form of film or injection-molded parts.

At or below room temperature the polymer is fully resistant in contact with water or water vapor; physical properties and dimensions remain unchanged indefinitely.

The effects of boiling water and steam are somewhat related to the processing history of the parts as well as to the purity of the polycarbonate used. Essentially stress-free solvent cast film changes its physical properties no more on long-term exposure to boiling water than it does with annealing in 100°C air (1) (section V, 6). Molded parts containing residual stresses, on the other hand, will show roughening of the surface, stress cracking, and turbidity after extending boiling (5), without evidence of appreciable chemical degradation.

Impurities in the resin, particularly those capable of an alkaline reaction, are known to reduce the resistance to steam and boiling water. Articles injection-molded from commercial bisphenol A polycarbonate, however, have ample stability to withstand the conditions normally encountered by tableware and household utensils for many years. They can also be repeatedly sterilized with steam up to 120°C in conventional equipment.

Molten polycarbonate is not stable in the presence of water vapor, which causes degradation by hydrolysis. Thorough drying of polycarbonate resins to a very low moisture content before thermoplastic processing is therefore mandatory (section V, 4 and Chapter VI).

The aromatic polycarbonates have good resistance to air, oxygen, and light. Annealing of solvent cast film in air at temperatures up to and above 150°C for extended periods reduces only the elongation (section V, 6), without a noticeable decrease in molecular weight (2) (Table V-26).

Solvent cast film made from uncontaminated bisphenol A polycarbonate has shown only very slight yellowing after extended exposure to temperatures in excess of 150°C. In actual installations the maximum continuous service temperature for parts made from this resin has been found to be about 135 to 140°C.

Bisphenol A polycarbonate displays remarkable resistance to ultraviolet radiation. Neither discoloring nor any change of physical properties, for example, was observed on a solvent cast film exposed for 72 hours at 45°C to an analytical lamp (Hanau 300) without filter (1). Exposure to ultraviolet radiation of a longer duration leads to crazing and molecular-weight degradation on the exposed surface of the parts. Since polycarbonate absorbs strongly in the ultraviolet range (section V, 8), the subsurface strata of the parts are protected so that there is no attack of the body of material (5). Bisphenol A polycarbonate furthermore is highly resistant to high-energy radiation (76,77) (section III, 3, A, 7, A).

In the temperate zone of central Europe the weathering resistance of bisphenol A polycarbonate in outdoor exposure to air, humidity, and light

TABLE V-26

Resistance of Aromatic Polycarbonate Film to Heat Aging in Air

Polycarbonate based on	Film thick-ness [μ]	Temper-ature [°C]	Time aged [weeks]	Tensile strength [kg/cm²]	Elonga-tion [%]
4,4'-Dihydroxy-diphenyl-2,2-propane	45	140	0	663	54
			8	749	7
			12	684	8
"	80	160	0	774	148
			8	647	58
			12	635	14
4,4'-Dihydroxy-diphenyl-1,1-cyclohexane	65	170	0	814	56
			4	769	8
4,4'-Dihydroxy-3,3',5,5'-tetrachloro-diphenyl-2,2-propane	60	190	0	1023	7
			4	1006	10
			8	1007	9

under varying temperature conditions is so good that for many applications stabilizers are not necessary. Samples of solvent cast film and injection-molded parts showed neither discoloration nor any significant changes in physical properties after one year weathering tests at Krefeld-Uerdingen. Oriented fibers also were not affected in a 9-month weathering test (2). In regions in which the intensity of sunlight is great surface effects of the kind observed under ultraviolet radiation will occur (5). Under such conditions the weathering properties may be improved by incorporating ultraviolet absorbers in the plastic or by protecting the parts with ultraviolet-absorbing coatings (5,78).

Samples buried in garden soil for one year showed no effects from soil corrosion agents, such as humic acids and microorganisms (2). Parts are also fungus-resistant in accordance with United States military specifications MIL-E-5272 c, MIL-E-4970 B, MIL-F-8261 A, and MIL-5422 E (5).

Bisphenol A polycarbonate is combustible. However, although thin films and fibers will support combustion, larger parts will not because of the material's high ignition temperature (above 500°C), poor thermal conductivity, and probably the fact that thermal decomposition releases carbon dioxide (79). Thus the polymer is classified as self-extinguishing in accordance with ASTM D 635 (5).

The stability of bisphenol A polycarbonate in aqueous solutions of inorganic and organic acids, salts, and oxidizing agents is very good. At room temperature solvent cast film samples showed no attack after 13 weeks immersion in a 20% solution of hydrochloric acid, hydrofluoric acid (40%), sulfuric acid (10–50%), nitric acid (20%), chromic acid (20%), arsenic acid (20%), phosphoric acid (conc.), formic acid (10–100%), acetic acid (20–100%), tartaric acid (30%), lactic acid (20%), citric acid (40%), and hydrogen peroxide (30%).

This polycarbonate is also fully resistant to aqueous solutions of weak alkalies, such as sodium carbonate and sodium bicarbonate. Organophilic bases, on the other hand, such as ammonium hydroxide and amines, are capable of saponifying the polycarbonate rapidly and completely back to bisphenol A (2). Aqueous solutions of strong alkalies will attack the surfaces of specimens and systematically break them down by saponification.

Stress-relieved injection-molded parts of bisphenol A polycarbonate were tested in saturated salt solutions for 6 months at 20°C and found to be resistant to aluminum chloride, aluminum sulfate, ammonium chloride, ammonium nitrate, ammonium sulfate, antimony trichloride, borax, calcium chloride, calcium nitrate, calcium sulfate, calcium hypochlorite, chrome alum, iron chloride, iron sulfate, potassium aluminum alum, potassum bichromate, potassium bromate, potassium bromide, potassium chloride, potassium nitrate, potassium thiocyanate, potassium perchlorate, potassium permanganate, potassium persulfate, potassium sulfate, cupric chloride, cuprous chloride, cupric sulfate, magnesium chloride, magnesium sulfate, manganese sulfate, sodium bisulfate, sodium bisulfite, sodium chlorate, sodium chloride, sodium hypochlorite, sodium sulfate, nickel sulfate, mercurous chloride, silver nitrate, mercuric chloride, stannous chloride, zinc chloride, and zinc sulfate (72).

The resistance of highly amorphous bisphenol A polycarbonate parts to organic solvents is rather limited. It is indifferent to aliphatic and cycloaliphatic hydrocarbons, mono- and polyfunctional alcohols with the exception of methanol, and vegetable and animal fats and oils. Most other organic solvents either swell or dissolve it (2) (section V, 1).

Very important for many commercial applications is the full resistance of this polymer to aqueous solutions of soaps, detergents, and bleaches fruit juices, alcoholic beverages, animal and vegetable fats, oils and waxes, photographic chemicals, all varieties of foodstuffs, and many disinfectants. Of particular advantage is its complete indifference to aqueous solutions of natural and synthetic dyes and pigments, which precludes the discoloration of parts by coffee, tea, fruit juices, ink, lipstick, etc.

11. PHYSIOLOGICAL PROPERTIES OF BISPHENOL A POLYCARBONATE

Parts made from commercial bisphenol A polycarbonate have found many applications in which they are in contact with food items, e.g., kitchen appliance components, dinnerware, milking-machine parts, packaging film, and bottles. The material is also used for dentures and artificial teeth, plasma containers, and in the packaging of pharmaceuticals. A necessary requirement common to all such applications is the absence of any biological activity of the plastic itself or any components extractable from it.

Bornmann and Loeser (80) investigated the biological activity of bisphenol A polycarbonate through animal experiments with rats. They observed no toxicological symptoms on subchronic feeding tests, chronic drinking water test, and individual acute ingestion tests.

In clinical tests and bisphenol A polycarbonate dentures no irritating effects to mucous membranes or toxicity of the plastic were observed. Nor have any other reports been forthcoming on a detrimental effect on the human organism after several years of experience with the processing of polycarbonates and their applications in a great variety of fields.

In accordance with the rules of "Gesundheitsblatt 1960," Nr. 26, p. 416, there are no reservations under German food law with regard to articles manufactured from 4,4'-dihydroxy-diphenyl-2,2-propane and 4,4'-dihydroxy-diphenyl-1,1-cyclohexane polycarbonates.

The U. S. Department of Health, Education, and Welfare—Food and Drug Administration—has ruled polycarbonates are safe for use in direct contact with all types of solid, liquid, fatty, and nonfatty foodstuffs. The classification covered by the listing numbered 121 2574 includes food containers and packages as well as components for food dispensers, processing equipment, and serving utensils (81).

The large-scale production of the polymer has furthermore invited investigations of the biological effects of bisphenol A.

Acute ingestion experiments with bisphenol A conducted on rats (oral administration of a 20% suspension in distilled water) indicated a lethal dose LD_{50} (7 days) of 4240 mg/kg. The diuretic effect of the material is about five times that of urea. Subcutaneous application of 2400 mg/kg (20% solution in 1,2-propylene glycol) produced an estrogenic effect in rats. With oral application, there was only a slight suggestion of this effect.

12. IDENTIFICATION OF POLYCARBONATES

The most straightforward method for the identification of an aromatic polycarbonate consists in determining its infrared absorption spectrum and comparing it with that of known polycarbonates (3) (section V, 8). Polycarbonates can also be hydrolyzed, e.g., with alcoholic potassium hydroxide, and the basic dihydroxy compounds can be isolated and identified (71). This method is particularly useful in the investigation of mixed polycarbonates produced from a number of different aromatic dihydroxy compounds or polycarbonates which contain, besides the carbonic acid radical, other dicarbonic acid groups. The suggestion has been made to interpret the greenish-blue color obtained by the introduction of pyrolysis vapors into a 1% solution of dimethylaminobenzaldehyde in methanol, and the subsequent change to dark blue when acidified with hydrochloric acid, as evidence of the presence of an aromatic polycarbonate (82). The pyrolysis products can also be characterized and at times identified by gas-liquid chromatography (83).

References

1. H. Schnell, *Angew. Chem.* **68**, 633 (1956).
2. II. Schnell, *Ind. Eng. Chem.* **51**, 157 (1959).
3. H. Schnell, *Plastics Inst. (London), Trans. J.* **28**, 143 (1960).
4. W. F. Christopher, *Soc. Plastics Eng. J.* **14**, 31 (June 1958).
5. W. F. Christopher and D. W. Fox, *Polycarbonates,* Reinhold, New York, 1962.
6. E. Jenckel and K. Ueberreiter, *Z. Physik. Chem.* **A182**, 361 (1938); H. A. Stuart, *Die Physik der Hochpolymeren,* Vol. III, Springer-Verlag, 1955, p. 608, 639.
7. J. W. Breitenbach, et al. *Die makrom. Chem.* **38**, 1 (1960); M. L. Huggins, *J. Polymer Sci.* **8**, 257 (1952).
8. G. V. Schulz and A. Horbach, *Die makrom. Chem.* **29**, 93 (1959); M. Tomikawa, *Chem. High Polymers Japan* **20**, 11 (1963) ref., *Die makrom. Chem.* **64**, 230 (1963).
9. G. Meyerhoff, *Z. Elektrochem.* **61**, 325 (1957).
10. O. Fuchs, *Z. Elektrochem.* **60**, 229 (1956); *Die makrom. Chem.* **5**, 245 (1950); **7**, 259 (1951).
11. G. F. Baumann and S. Steingiser, *J. Polymer Sci.* A 1, 3395 (1963).
12. G. V. Schulz, *Z. physik. Chem.* **B43**, 25 (1939); **47**, 155 (1940); *Z. Elektrochem.* **60**, 199 (1956).
13. A. V. Tobolsky, *Properties and Structure of Polymers,* John Wiley and Sons, New York, 1960, p. 302.
14. D. R. Morey and J. W. Tamblyn, *J. Appl. Phys.* **16**, 419 (1945); H. A. Stuart, *Die Physik der Hochpolymeren,* Vol. II, Springer-Verlag, 1953, p. 751.
15. S. Kroser, M. Veinrieb, and L. Silina, *Vysokomolekul. Soedin,* **2**, 1876 (1960).
16. G. Meyerhoff, *Die makrom. Chem.* **6'** 197 (1951).

17. G. V. Schulz and G. Meyerhoff, *Z. Elektrochem.* **56**, 545 (1952); G. Meyerhoff, Houben-Weyl *Methoden der organischen Chemie*, Vol. III, Part 1, Georg Thieme-Verlag, Stuttgart, 1955, p. 393.
18. A. de Chirico, *Chim. Ind.* **42**, 248 (1960).
19. J. W. Breitenbach and E. L. Forster, *Oesterr. Chem. Ztg.* **54**, 346 (1953); **56**, 93 (1955).
20. G. Meyerhoff, *Z. Naturforsch.* **11b**, 302 (1956).
21. G. V. Schulz, *Z. Naturforsch.* **2a**, 348 (1947).
22. G. V. Schulz and F. Blaschke, *J. Prakt. Chem.* [*2*] **158**, 130 (1941); G. V. Schulz and G. Sing, *J. Prakt. Chem.* [*2*] **161**, 161 (1943).
23. M. L. Huggins, *J. Am. Chem. Soc.* **64**, 2716 (1942).
24. J. G. Kirkwood and J. Riseman, *J. Chem. Phys.* **16**, 565 (1948).
25. P. Debye and A. M. Bueche, *J. Chem. Phys.* **16**, 573 (1948); A. Peterlin, *J. Colloid. Sci.* **10**, 587 (1955); *Die makrom. Chem.* **18/19**, 254 (1956).
26. T. G Fox, Jr., and P. J. Flory, *J. Am. Chem. Soc.* **73**, 1915 (1951); P. J. Flory, *Principles of Polymer Chemistry,* Cornell University Press, 1953.
27. B. H. Zimm, W. H. Stockmayer, and M. Fixman, *J. Chem. Phys.* **21**, 1716 (1953).
28. S. N. Chinai, P. C. Scherer, C. W. Bondurant, and D. W. Levi, *J. Polymer Sci.* **22**, 527 (1956).
29. R. I. Thompson and K. B. Goldblum, *Mod. Plastics* **35**, 131 (April 1958).
30. A. Prietzschk, *Kolloid-Z.* **156**, 8 (1958).
31. P. H. Hermans and A. Weidinger, *J. Appl. Phys.* **19**, 491 (1948).
32. P. H. Hermans and H. Weidinger, *Die makrom. Chem.* **64**, 135 (1963).
33. L. Bottenbruch, H. Schnell, and A. Prietzschk (to Farbenfabriken Bayer A. G.), Belg. Pat. 589,858 (1960).
34. G. Kämpf, *Kolloid-Z.* **172**, 50 (1960); **185**, 6 (1962).
35. R. Eppe, E. W. Fischer, and H. A. Stuart, *J. Polymer Sci.* **34**, 721 (1959).
36. L. Makavuk, J. V. Koslov, and V. A. Kargin, *Vysokomolekul. Soedin.* **2**, 931 (1960).
37. A. Reichle and H. Wilsing (to Farbenfabriken Bayer A. G.), U. S. Pat. 3,005,236 (1961); A. Prietzschk and H. Marzolph (to Farbenfabriken Bayer A. G.), Belg. Pat. 564,009 (1958).
38. U. Veiel, A. Prietzschk, and H. Schnell (to Farbenfabriken Bayer A. G.), U. S. Pat. 3,007, 204 (1961).
39. W. Hechelhammer and G. Peilstöcker, *Kunststoffe* **49**, 3 and 93 (1959).
40. G. Peilstöcker, *Kunststoffe* **51**, 509 (1961).
41. Anon., *Brit. Plastics* **31**, 112 (March 1958).
42. K. B. Goldblum, *Corrosion* **14**, 90 (July 1958).
43. H. Gadd, K. B. Goldblum, and W. R. Christopher, *Canad. Plastics,* 34 (May 1959).
44. Anon., *Mod. Plastics* **37**, 10 (1959).
45. E. E. Hardy, in Kirk Othmer, *Encyclopedia of Chemical Technology,* 2nd Suppl. vol., Interscience Publishers, New York, 1960, p. 587.
46. V. E. Yarsley, *Kunstoff-Rundschau* **8**, 165 (1961).
47. Anon., *Mod. Plastics* **37**, 164 (January 1960).
48. I. P. Locev, O. V. Smirnova, and E. V. Smurova, *Plasticheskie Massy* **9**, 10 (1962).
49. C. A. Brighton and S. J. Skinner, *Plastics Inst. (London), Trans. J.* **31**, 70 (June 1963).

50. Polycarbonatspritzgussmassen, DIN 7744 (August 1961).
51. J. V. Roslov, L. Makavuk, V. N. Fonin, and V. N. Olchovskij, *Vysokomolekul. Soedin.* **2**, 770 (1960).
52. G. Peilstöcker, *Kunststoffe* **51**, 509 (1961).
53. W. Knappe, *Kunststoffe* **51**, 707 (1961).
54. K. H. Hellwege, J. Hennig, and W. Knappe, *Kolloid-Z., Z. Polymere* **188**, 121 (1963).
55. K. H. Hellwege, W. Knappe, and W. Wetzel, *Kolloid-Z.* **180**, 126 (1962); K. H. Hellwege, J. Hennig, and W. Knappe, *Kolloid-Z.* **186**, 29 (1962).
46. Anon., *Mod. Plastics* **39**, 98 (March 1962); Anon., *Kunstostoffberater* **6**, 643 (1961).
57. K. H. Illers and H. Breuer, *Kolloid-Z.* **176**, 110 (1961).
58. F. P. Reding, I. A. Faucher, and R. D. Whitman, *J. Polymer Sci.* **54**, 56 (1961).
59. H. Hofmeier, *Angew. Chem.* **74**, 647 (1962); *Elektrotech. Z.* **B14**, 601 (1962).
60. H. Schnell (to Farbenfabriken Bayer A. G.), Ger. Pat. 962,274 (1957).
61. H. Schnell (to Farbenfabriken Bayer A. G.), Ger. Pat. 1,016,784 (1962).
62. H. Hofmeier, *Elektrotech. Z.* **11**, 412 (1959).
63. Anon., *Mod. Plastics* **37**, 90 (November 1959).
64. B. M. Kovarskaja, *Plasticheskie Massy* **10**, 11 (1962).
65. A. Hersping, *Kunststoffe* **52**, 73 (1962).
66. F. Krum and F. H. Müller, *Kolloid-Z.* **164**, 81 (1959).
67. F. M. Müller and K. Huff, *Kolloid-Z.* **164**, 34 (1959).
68. F. Krum, *Kolloid-Z.* **165**, 77 (1959).
69. H. Hofmeier, *Kunststoffberater* **5**, 350 (1960).
70. G. P. Michailov and M. P. Eidelnant, *Vysokomolekul. Soedin.* **2**, 287 (1960).
71. D. Hümmel, *Kunststoff-Lack-und Gummianalyse,* Karl Hanser-Verlag, München, (1958), p. 201.
72. Firmenschrift "Makrolon" der Farbenfabriken Bayer A. G. (1960).
73. B. G. Achhammer, M. Tryon, and G. M. Kline, *Mod. Plastics* **37**, 131 (December 1959); *Kunststoffe* **49**, 600 (1959).
74. Anon. *Chem. Eng. News* **40**, No. 38, 60 (1962).
75. O. K. Spürr, Jr. and W. D. Niegisch, *J. Appl. Polymer Sci.* **6**, 585 (1962).
76. R. C. Giberson, *Mod. Plastics,* **143**, (April 1962).
77. V. J. Krasnansky, B. G. Achhamer, and M. S. Parker, *SPE Trans.* **1**, 133 (July 1961).
78. M. Pestemer, W. Siefken, and O. Bayer (to Farbenfabriken Bayer A. G.), U. S. Pat. 2,965,578 (1960).
79. M. Tomikawa, *Chem. High Polymers Japan* **20**, 102 (1963); ref. *Die makrom. Chem.* **65**, 252 (1963).
80. G. Bornmann and A. Loeser, *Arzneimittel-Forschg. (Drug Research)* **9**, 9 (1959).
81. Anon., *Chemical Horizons* **2**, No. 23, 91 (June 6, 1963); *J. Commerce,* 9 (May 27, 1963); *Federal Register* (May 22, 1963); 28 F.R. 5083.
82. L. Placzek, *Kunststoffe* **50**, 174 (1960).
83. W. H. Parriss and P. D. Holland, *Brit. Plastics* **33**, 372 (1960).

VI. THE MANUFACTURE AND USE OF BISPHENOL A POLYCARBONATE PARTS

Among the large number of aromatic polycarbonates produced and investigated in the laboratory only the bisphenol A polycarbonates and some copolymers based predominantly on bisphenol A have found application on a commercial scale. The reasons for this are mainly of an economic nature. Commercial quantities of bisphenol A of the required purity are easily produced from inexpensive raw materials of which there is an unlimited supply (section IV, 1, A). Although certain other aromatic polycarbonates and polycarbonate copolymers display properties even more desirable for certain specific applications than those of the bisphenol A based polymer, their commercial debut will be determined primarily by whether or not economical processes can be developed for the production of the necessary aromatic dihydroxy compounds.

The manufacturing methods, which are described in the following pages as they apply to bisphenol A polycarbonates, are not limited to this specific material. Those that start with a polymer solution are equally applicable to other aromatic polycarbonates soluble in suitable solvents (section V, 1). Methods wherein the polymer passes through the molten state may be employed with any aromatic polycarbonate melting below approximately 300°C (section V, 2). Since bisphenol A polycarbonate is both soluble in suitable solvents, particularly methylene chloride, and thermally stable as a melt, it can be used to produce an almost unlimited variety of parts and products by any one of the solution and thermoplastic processes common in the plastics industry.

The areas of application for these parts and products are determined by the specific properties of this polycarbonate, which include desirable mechanical properties over an unusually wide temperature range, very low tendency to cold flow, high continuous service temperatures, excellent electrical properties up to high temperatures, low moisture absorption, good dimensional stability, transparency, good weathering properties, physiological indifference, and resistance to water, acids, oxidizing and reducing chemicals, salt solutions, oils, fats, and aliphatic hydrocarbons; this combination of properties is not found in any other plastic.

Disadvantages, on the other hand, which limit the usefulness of this material in certain applications, are its solubility in many organic solvents, a susceptibility of stress-cracking due to internal stresses or under external loads, particularly in the presence of solvents or solvent vapors, as well as a certain tendency toward fatigue failure under a continuous dynamic load.

Bisphenol A polycarbonates have been introduced in many fields, including, to name a few, the electrical industry, appliances, tableware, industrial equipment, automotive parts, office machines, lighting fixtures, photographic equipment, building construction materials, pharmaceutical and medical supplies, dentures, cosmetic supplies, musical instruments, records, toys, and packaging.

Successful inroads into new areas of application and substantial increases in the quantities that can be produced and sold will depend, for one thing, on the development of economical processes for the manufacture of oriented film and fibers with optimum properties, but even more so, of course, on the ultimate sales price of the polymer.

The following sections are devoted to a brief description of the methods used in manufacturing bisphenol A polycarbonate products and some of the applications to which they have been put.

1. FILM AND FIBERS

Basically, both solution and thermoplastic processes are suitable for making bisphenol A polycarbonate film and fibers. A large portion of the film produced commercially today is cast from solution, since this method can most easily ensure the high degree of uniformity, transparency, optical clarity, and absence of color and foreign particles that are required for electrical insulation and photographic base material. In addition, the solvent-casting technique makes it possible to employ very high molecular weight polycarbonate, which, because of its high-melt viscosity, can be processed by thermoplastic methods only with difficulty or not at all. Methylene chloride is particularly well suited for solvent-casting operations.

The thickness to which clear transparent bisphenol A polycarbonate film can be cast is not unlimited. Above a certain critical thickness a hazy film is obtained. The critical thickness varies, among other things, with average molecular weight, molecular weight distribution, and conditions maintained during the casting process. The film appears hazy as the result of crystallites which have grown larger than the wavelength of the visible spectrum (section V, 5).

Crystallization may be suppressed, and the critical film thickness thus increased, by using polycarbonates with higher molecular weight or polycarbonate copolymers with reduced crystallization tendencies or by more rapid evaporation of the solvent in the casting operation.

Conventional belt- and drum-type casting machines will produce optically clear film up to 250 μ in thickness from bisphenol A polycarbonates (1) with (determined by solution viscosity) molecular weights of 74,000 to 91,000; solutions with solid content up to 25% can be handled.

More concentrated solutions have a tendency to gel in storage. Optically clear film of 300 μ and thicker can be cast from solutions of polycarbonate copolymers in which either a portion of the bisphenol A has been replaced by bulky or asymmetrical aromatic dihydroxy compounds or the residues of bulky or asymmetrical dicarbonic acids have taken the place of some of the carbonic acid residues. However, extrusion of the molten polycarbonate through sheeting dies is usually better suited for the production of thicker film and plate (section VI, 2). At the lower end of the scale the thickness of solvent cast film is limited only by handling difficulties.

Extremely thin film (less than 6 μ) is cast onto a carrier film from which it is not separated before the final manufacturing step, e.g., in winding capacitors.

Thin film can also be produced from the melt by the blow-molding technique (section VI, 2).

The electrical industry uses unoriented, largely amorphous solvent cast bisphenol A polycarbonate film ranging from 20 to 200 μ in thickness as insulating material for wires and coils (form, layer, and covering insulation) and for slot insulation in fractional horsepower motors (2,3).

Insulators vacuum-formed from polycarbonate film have been used successfully for insulating intricately shaped magnet cores (section VI, 2).

Film of less than 10 μ thickness can be produced in a simple manner, without violating the tolerance requirements of capacitor insulation, by cold drawing a thicker film in one direction without simultaneous crystallization. This film can be shrunk by short-term heating to 150–160°C, in which the orientation disappears. This is of particular advantage in winding capacitors, since it makes it possible to shrink the completed assemblies. In addition, these oriented films display higher ultimate tensile strength and reduced elongation in the draw direction (section V, 6) (4).

Experiments conducted by McLean, Wehe, and Dante (5) have shown that bisphenol A polycarbonate film used as the dielectric in capacitors has particular advantages over other insulating film with regard to high insulation resistance, low dielectric loss, extremely low temperature co-efficient of capacitance above room temperature, and minimal change of insulating resistance and capacitance with moisture. For applications requiring high mechanical strength in addition to good electrical properties unidirectionally stretched and crystallized insulating film has recently become commercially available (4).

Nonstretched, highly amorphous solvent cast bisphenol A polycarbonate film, colorless, transparent, and distinguished by high mechanical strength, low water absorption, and dimensional stability under varying moisture and temperature conditions, is very well suited as a carrier for photographic emulsions (6).

Processes have been developed which improve the bond between the hydrophilic gelatin-base silver-halide emulsions used in photographic film and the hydrophobic polycarbonate film, as well as between the rear layers and the hydrophobic polycarbonate film by the use of suitable interlayers (7,8). The fact that bisphenol A polycarbonate film, in spite of its many advantages over cellulose acetate, has not found large scale acceptance for amateur photographic and movie film use is due primarily to commercial considerations.

Solvent cast film between 100 and 200 μ thick is used as commercial photographic film in reproduction work (9). For such applications the dimensional stability of the film, regardless of variations in moisture and temperature conditions, as well as its ability to resist deformation by the hydrophilic photographic layers as they swell and dry during processing are of particular importance.

In order for very thin films to be able to absorb the aforementioned forces without deformation, a high modulus of elasticity is desired. Several aromatic polycarbonate copolymers and block-copolymers have therefore been developed, which will yield film having a higher modulus of elasticity than that normally measured on bisphenol A polycarbonate film (section III, 3, A, 6).

Solvent cast bisphenol A polycarbonate film with a matt finish is well suited for use as drafting film, again because its dimensions are unaffected by moisture and temperature variations. Such film is easily produced by casting the solution onto a surface having the necessary roughness. Another method used to impart a rough or matt surface finish to polycarbonate film or parts consists of a short-time treatment in an alkali or alkaline earth hydroxide solution at elevated temperature (10).

Aromatic polycarbonates have also been suggested for use as magnetic record carriers (magnetic tape) (11).

Economic considerations as a rule suggest thermoplastic processes, i.e., blow or sheet die extrusion, in preference to solvent casting for the production of bisphenol A polycarbonate film intended for packaging. Film so obtained is distinguished by optical clarity, high surface gloss, dimensional stability, desirable mechanical and electrical properties, resistance to high temperatures, and insensitiveness to moisture. Furthermore, it is impermeable to oils and fats, contains no plasticizers, has no odor or taste, is physiologically inert, and can be sterilized (12).

Polycarbonate film can without difficulty be printed on, cemented (13), and heat-sealed by simple conventional methods, which present advantages, whether the application is as packaging material, electrical insulation, photoemulsion base, or magnetic tape.

Bisphenol A polycarbonate film, if it is free of internal stress, can itself be bonded under pressure after having been swollen with a solvent such as methylene chloride or some swelling agents. It can also be cemented to cellulose acetate film with a suitable isocyanate adhesive (14).

Nonstretched film can be heat-sealed with conventional equipment without difficulty, provided it has been thoroughly dried to prevent chemical degradation. High-frequency heat sealing is also possible in spite of the small dielectric loss angle, but specialized equipment is required (15).

Vacuum-forming techniques have been used very successfully to produce molded articles from bisphenol A polycarbonate film, sheet, and plate for use in electrical equipment, in light fixtures, and as containers (16). The polymer lends itself particularly well to this technique (17) because of its well-defined plastic range between the second-order transition temperature (149°C) and the melting range (220–230°C). Both straight vacuum forming and drape and vacuum forming can be used to process film or sheets at a drawing temperature of approximately 180°C, giving exact duplication of mold shape and uniformity of wall thickness; only short heating times are required. To avoid degradation and the formation of bubbles in the material the film must be stored dry or redried prior to processing (18).

Conventional vacuum metallizing technology is applicable to aromatic polycarbonate film without any particular difficulty.

Stretched and crystallized fibers, as well as film stretched in two perpendicular directions and crystallized, are in the development stage.

2. INJECTION-MOLDED PARTS, EXTRUDED TUBES AND SHAPES, AND BLOW-MOLDED ARTICLES

A. Injection Molding

The largest portion by far of the commercially produced bisphenol A polycarbonate is converted into parts and finished products by thermoplastic processing methods (19–31). Thermoplastic processing of the material utilizes the conventional equipment of the plastics industry, such as injection-molding machines and extruders.

Molding grade bisphenol A polycarbonates have average molecular weights (calculated from solution viscosity) between 32,000 and 35,000. The melt viscosities of higher molecular products exceed the limits of economical processing methods.

The temperature range available for processing extends from 240 to 330°C. In this range the polycarbonate will not suffer any noticeable degradation so long as it contains less than approximately 0.01% moisture (section V, 4). Excessive moisture causes chemical degradation as melt temperatures are reached, with bubbles forming in the molten material. Additives such as lead or zinc silicates, organic tin compounds, aryl tin oxides (32), or tertiary esters of phosphorous acid with aromatic hydroxy compounds, such as tris-2-*tert.*-butyl-5-methyl-phenyl phosphite, have been suggested for stabilizing aromatic polycarbonates against degradation or discoloration at elevated temperatures (33).

The low moisture content necessary for thermoplastic processing is obtained by drying for about 8 hours at 120°C in a convection or vacuum oven. Since the dry polymer will rapidly absorb water from the air, it is recommended to keep it hot until it is transferred to the heated feed hopper of the processing unit.

Dry polycarbonate delivered in vacuum-tight containers is heated to about 110°C before breaking the seal in order to avoid moisture pick-up during handling and transfer.

Polycarbonate produced by the phosgenation process must be essentially free of chlorocarbonic acid ester groups. Methylene chloride used as a solvent also needs to have been removed down to very low residual values, since methylene chloride decomposes to form hydrochloric acid at the thermoplastic processing temperatures under the catalytic effect of metal surfaces. Hydrochloric acid resulting from the breakdown of chlorocarbonic acid ester end groups and methylene chloride causes corrosion of the processing equipment and the molds and is further capable of changing the character of certain dyes and pigments.

In the form of largely amorphous pellets obtained by extruding strands and subsequently cutting them bisphenol A polycarbonate can be processed on all commercial injection-molding machines designed to attain barrel temperatures of about 350°C. In order to prevent moisture absorption by the pellets during their residence time in the feed hopper, the cover is heated by means of radiation equipment. A heating capacity of about 3000 watt/m² is usually sufficient.

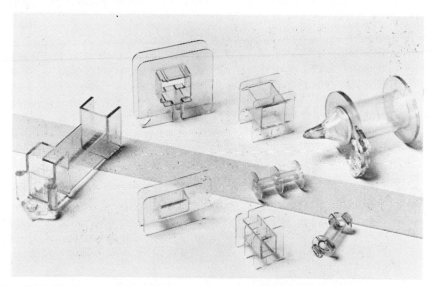

Fig. VI-1. Small components for the electrical industry injection-molded of bisphenol A polycarbonate.

For larger parts screw-injection-molding machines are required. High injection pressures, in the range of 700 to 2200 kg/cm², are necessitated by the high-melt viscosity of polycarbonate. Nozzles, whether of the open or the automatic shutoff type, must be heated, preferably to cylinder temperature.

Die designs must make allowance for the high-melt viscosity of polycarbonate by providing short sprues of ample cross-sectional area, making runners as short as possible, and keeping wall thickness above 0.7 mm. Molds should be heated to improve mold flow and reduce internal stresses within the parts. Mold temperatures as high as 120°C are possible in view of the high second-order transition temperature; as a rule, internal stresses can be reduced by heating molds above 80°C.

The rigidity and dimensional stability of the molded parts prevents their removal from undercut molds. This, as well as the inevitable mold shrinkage of about 0.8%, must be taken into account in the design of the die.

Mold inserts must be heated to temperatures above 100°C if stress cracks in the molded parts are to be avoided. Hardened steels are suitable for mold construction. Chrome plating is not required. Good polish of the mold interior is important in order to obtain parts with glossy surfaces.

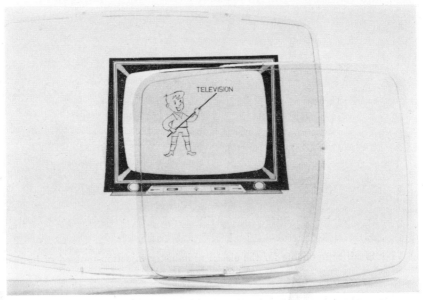

Fig. VI-2. TV tube safety shields injection-molded of bisphenol A polycarbonate.

During short-term interruptions of injection-molding operations the cylinder temperature should not be allowed to fall below 160°C; otherwise there is danger that polycarbonate adhering to the cylinder walls may pull off parts of the oxide layer on contraction. For the same reason it is recommended that the cylinder of polycarbonate be purged before shutdown by using some other high-melt viscosity thermoplastic (e.g., polyethylene).

Parts produced by injection molding are distinguished by high surface glass and a pleasing feel.

Colored pellets are used to produce both opaque and transparent parts in a multitude of colors. In selecting dyes and pigments, their stability at the high processing temperatures must be considered (34).

Molded parts can also be dyed in aqueous dyeing solutions.

Injection-molded bisphenol A polycarbonate parts have proved themselves in actual service in many fields (35–42). The most important applications are in the electrical industry (radio, phono, TV, communica-

Fig. VI-3. Injection-molded bisphenol A polycarbonate dinnerware.

tions), where they have been used as enclosures, guards, safety shields for TV tubes, components, such as printed circuit boards, coil forms, plugs, terminal boards, telephone housings, accessories, battery cases and lids, terminal covers, acid level gages, distributor covers; in the industrial equipment line, as precision parts for instruments and controls, typewriters, calculators, and fans; in the home, as components of kitchen appliances, refrigerators, freezers, and domestic heaters, as well as in dishes and camping utensils; on the farm, as parts of milking equipment; in the medical supply field, as Petri dishes, blood filters, and cases for dental drills; in the office, as drafting equipment, slide rules, and templates; in industrial safety equipment, as safety helmets and parts of mine helmets; in the lighting industry, as street-light lenses and neon-tube sockets; in the photographic industry, as camera and lightmeter housings; and in the automotive industry, as transparent covers, indicator lights, directional signal-light lenses, distribution boxes, instrument housings, and guards (Figs. VI-1 to VI-4).

Simple injection-molding equipment has been developed for use in the dental laboratory. In these units bisphenol A polycarbonate can be

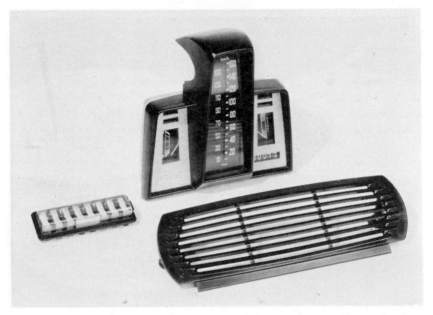

Fig. VI-4. Injection-molded bisphenol A polycarbonate parts for the automotive industry.

melted and injected under pressure into plaster molds of teeth and associated supporting structures, such as clasps. Dentures made from this polycarbonate are distinguished by excellent dimensional stability, regardless of variations in temperature and moisture, good mechanical properties, and high elasticity. They will not discolor, and they can be underlined and repaired with any one of the cold- or hot-curing poly-(methyl methacrylate) base plastics commonly used in denture work (43,44).

B. Extrusion

Conventional techniques and equipment are used in the production of bisphenol A polycarbonate pipe, rods, shapes, sheets, film, and various tubular products by extrusion. Every type of extruder developed for thermoplastic material is suitable. Screws, which need not be equipped for heating or cooling, should have a length of at least 15 L/D. Hardened steel single-flight screws with constant pitch and progressive root diameter are used with best results.

A compression ratio of 1:2.4 is desirable. Again a moisture content of the feed polycarbonate below 0.01% must be ensured by following the recommendations given in the section on injection molding.

Processing temperatures range from 240 to 300°C. A smooth temperature increase from the feed throat to the tip of the screw, followed by a slightly lower die temperature, has been found most expedient. This favors uniform pressure buildup along the barrel; higher back-pressures can be obtained with screen packs or valves consisting of an annular restriction adjustable by axial positioning of the screw. Higher back-pressures improve plasticization and reduce the formation of bubbles.

The polycarbonate melt must leave the extruder in clear transparent and bubble-free strands. Again, as recommended for injection-molding operations, the barrel temperature should be reduced to about 160°C, if it is necessary to interrupt an extruder run temporarily, and shutdown should be preceded by flushing with some other high viscosity thermoplastic material such as polyethylene.

In the extrusion of tubular products both vacuum-forming dies and high-pressure floating mandrel techniques can be used. The relatively high-melt viscosity of the material is an advantage in both processes, so that tube and pipe of a wide range of diameters and wall thicknesses are produced without difficulty (Fig. VI-5).

In order to avoid the formation of internal stresses, it was also found desirable not to chill the tubes as they leave the die but rather to adjust the environment within a short distance from the front end of the extruder to a temperature of 80 to 100°C (45).

The wall thickness of bisphenol A polycarbonate tubing and pipe can be kept lower than those conventionally used with other plastics, thanks to the superior mechanical strength and better cold-flow properties of the material. Finished pipe can be cemented and welded (heat-sealed).

Bisphenol A polycarbonate pipe has been successfully used in food applications for conveying fruit juices, beer, wine, milk, etc., for which its sterilizability, absence of taste and odor, biological inertness, and resistance to color pick-up make it eminently suitable.

With properly designed dies and take-up equipment, no undue difficulties are encountered in the continuous extrusion of shapes and profiles or in the continuous and discontinuous extrusion of semifinished goods, such as bar stock and block material.

In the production of sheet stock or plate by extrusion through a flat sheet die it must be remembered that the extruded product can be passed

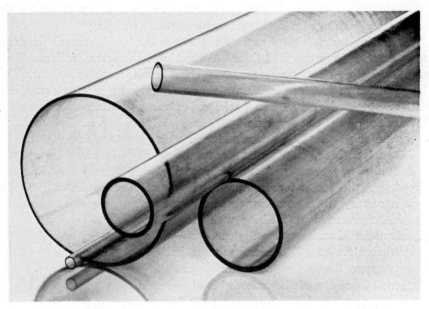

Fig. VI-5. Continuously extruded bisphenol A polycarbonate pipes.

around take-up rolls only if the rolls are heated to at least 130°C. At lower temperatures the material is too rigid because of the high second-order transition temperature (Fig. VI-6).

Free take-up, using cooled conveyor grating, can be employed.

Film extrusion through a flat die also requires heated take-up rolls. Blow extrusion of film, which involves the expansion of an extruded tube with compressed air, is carried out on conventional equipment without difficulty because of the high-melt viscosity and the wide plastic range of polycarbonate.

Fig. VI-6. Bisphenol A polycarbonate plates produced by thermoplastic fabrication methods.

Hollow shapes, particularly bottles, may be produced by blowing up a short piece of extruded tube inside a mold (blow molding) before the material leaves the plastic state (46).

Bisphenol A polycarbonate bottles, being transparent, dimensionally rigid even if thin walled, unbreakable, taste- and odor-free, sterilizable, and biologically inert, have been successfully adapted to a great number of applications, including many in which they have been used as containers for pharmaceutical and cosmetic products as well as for various foods and condiments.

A hand-operated miniature extruder, electrically heated with household current, has been developed for filling dental cavities with molten bisphenol A polycarbonate in the dentist's office. Fillings made of this polycarbonate seal well at the edges, are dimensionally stable under varying temperature and moisture conditions, will not discolor, and have good durability and abrasion resistance (47).

C. Compression Molding

Bisphenol A polycarbonate parts can also be produced by the compression-molding processes which have been developed primarily for thermosetting plastics. When techniques of this kind are used, a particular advantage is found in the fact that the high second-order transition temperature makes it possible to remove the parts from the mold as soon as they have cooled to 120 to 135°C.

Clear transparent panels with excellent surfaces are produced from pellets or sheet blanks by compression molding (Fig. VI-6).

D. Machining

Most metal- and wood-working tools and machines can be used without difficulty for machining bisphenol A polycarbonate parts or stock.

Overheating of the polycarbonate in the cutting area to a point at which softening sets in must be avoided by using low cutting speeds or by external cooling, e.g., with cooling oils. The polycarbonate may be turned, drilled, milled, sawed, sheared, punched, ground, polished, and cut on a shaper.

Polycarbonate parts can be attached to other materials or joined together with nails and rivets.

E. Cold Forming

The combination of properties characteristic of bisphenol A polycarbonate—ductility, low elastic elongation at the yield point, high rigidity, high modulus of elasticity, low cold flow, and high heat distortion temperature—makes it possible to apply to this plastic the cold-forming techniques developed in the metal-working industry.

Polycarbonate can be coined, rolled, riveted, and deep-drawn. As compared to many metals, however, the amount of cold deformation permissible is rather limited. As the original thickness of blanks is reduced to less than about 30% by cold forming, the incidence of breakage becomes significant.

A small amount of deformation increases the ball indentation hardness which, however, returns to its original value as the degree of deformation is further increased.

Other physical properties also change somewhat with the amount of deformation the material has had to undergo, but there is no over-all detrimental effect (20).

The technology of cold-forming thermoplastic materials is still very young. Only little has been learned about commercial applications (20,48).

Records produced by embossing bisphenol A polycarbonate disks show excellent audio reproduction, high- and low-temperature stability, and minimal wear as well as being virtually unbreakable.

F. Cementing, Welding, and Printing

Bisphenol A polycarbonate parts can be hot-air welded by using, if necessary, a welding rod of the same material. In order to avoid chemical degradation, drying of the parts to be joined, and particularly the welding rod, is recommended.

Cementing of bisphenol A polycarbonate parts is also possible with solvents or swelling agents, such as ethylene chloride, benzene, or styrene, or with specially formulated adhesives. If the parts contain internal stresses, however, there is the danger of stress-cracking at the cemented joints.

Many conventional lacquers, paints, and printing inks adhere well to the surfaces of bisphenol A polycarbonate parts.

G. Foaming

Most of the conventional foaming agents containing nitrogen, such as azo-bis-isobutyronitrile or benzosulfonic acid hydrazide, are unsuitable for the production of foams from bisphenol A polycarbonates, since they themselves or their decomposition products have the capacity to degrade and discolor the polycarbonate at the temperatures required to achieve foaming. These problems are avoided if monomers or polymers containing carboxylic acid carbonic acid anhydride groups are used as foaming agents for aromatic polycarbonates (49). Compounds of this nature, such as the anhydride of isophthalic acid bis-carbonic acid methyl ester or the carboxylic acid carbonic acid anhydride polymer obtained from

isophthalic acid and the bis-chlorocarbonic acid ester of bisphenol A, will split off CO_2 at elevated temperatures and thus form esters or polyesters. Mixtures of such substances and aromatic polycarbonates heated above the softening point of the polycarbonate will be foamed by the carbon dioxide released in the decomposition of the carboxylic acid carbonic acid anhydride group. The esters or polyesters remaining behind from this reaction are compatible with the polycarbonate.

It is also possible to build polyester copolymers on the basis of aromatic dihydroxy compounds in such a way that they contain, besides a large number of carbonic acid ester groups, a certain portion of carboxylic acid carbonic acid anhydride groups. When these copolymers are heated, they convert, essentially without molecular weight degradation, to polyester copolymers containing no more alien substances; at the same time they are foamed by the carbon dioxide released in the reaction (49).

Another technique for producing polycarbonate foams involves mixing the molten polymer under pressure with an inert solvent having a suitable boiling point, or with some inert gas, and letting the mixture cool while pressure is maintained. When this material is later heated in open molds (sometimes after having first undergone some suitable size reduction step) to a temperature above the softening point of the polymer, foaming will occur as the result of evaporation of the solvent or expansion of the trapped gas.

To foam bisphenol A polycarbonate by this method, aliphatic and cycloaliphatic hydrocarbons can be used as foaming agents. Combining 15 to 25 weight per cent cyclohexane with molten polycarbonate by mixing at 230 to 240°C and 280–psi produces, after the mass has cooled under pressure, colorless transparent pieces of material. Heated to 150°C, either in its original form or after having been ground up, this material converts to small-cell foam ranging from 0.05 to 0.25 g/cm³ in density (50).

Bisphenol A polycarbonate foams are distinguished by high-temperature stability, low heat conductivity, high mechanical strength even at low densities, desirable electrical properties, and good resistance to aging.

3. AROMATIC POLYCARBONATE PAINTS AND COATINGS

A number of aromatic polycarbonates and copolycarbonates, such as polycarbonates based on 4,4'-dihydroxy-diphenyl-2,2-butane or copolymers obtained from bisphenol A and 4,4'-dihydroxy-diphenyl-1,1-cyclohexane, are soluble in some of the solvents commonly employed in the paint industry (section V, 1). These products may be used as binders in physically drying coatings. The dried films exhibit high elasticity, excellent moisture resistance, low moisture absorption, high gloss, good resistance to outdoor light and weather exposure, and desirable electrical characteristics which extend to high temperatures.

The pigment-carrying capacity is good. Hardness and adhesion to metal surfaces are adequate. The latter two properties may be improved by heating the coated parts to temperatures above 140°C. The aromatic polycarbonates are compatible with a number of plasticizers, such as dibutylphthalate, benzyl-butyl phthalate, dioctyl phthalate, tricresyl phosphate, benzyl-butyl adipinate, benzyl-octyl adipinate, chlorinated diphenyl derivatives, and polymer plasticizers based on polyesters (51–53).

The fact that, in spite of their desirable properties, the aromatic polycarbonates have so far been accepted as a coating material only to a limited extent in the field of insulating coatings for the electrical industry is due, aside from the price situation, to the low solids content of solutions (25–30%) and the incompatibility of the aromatic polycarbonates with most other coating binders and resins.

Other potential applications for soluble aromatic polycarbonates are found in the manufacture of orally administered medicines with protractive action, in which the active ingredients are covered with a thin coat of polycarbonate (54), and in the production of light-transmitting layers for electrophotography, in which aromatic polycarbonates are used as binders (55).

Absorbent surfaces can be coated with aqueous dispersions of aromatic polycarbonates. Such dispersions are obtained by mixing water into highly concentrated solutions of aromatic polycarbonates in solvents which are not miscible with water, in the presence of emulsifiers (56).

Powders of aromatic polycarbonates, obtained easily either by mechanical grinding of a polymer, which has been somewhat swollen with a solvent or swelling agent (57) or by precipitation from solution with a nonsolvent (section III, 3, A, 3), can be used to coat metal parts by the fluid-bed sintering process.

This method, in which the part to be coated is preheated above the melting point of the aromatic polycarbonate and then submerged into a bed of polycarbonate powder fluidized with an inert gas, permits the application of relatively thick and tightly adhering smooth coatings without the use of a solvent. However, since the coefficients of thermal expansion of metal and polycarbonate are different, there is some danger of stress-cracking as the parts are cooled to room temperature (20).

References

1. G. Bier and H. Schnell in K. Winnacker and L. Küchler, ed., *Chemische Technologie,* Carl Hanser-Verlag, München, 1960, p. 299.
2. H. Schnell (to Farbenfabriken Bayer A. G.), Ger. Pats. 962,274 (1957), 1,010,784 (1962).

3. N. Parkman, *Plastics Inst. (London), Trans. J.* **29**, 73 (1961).
4. H. Hofmeier, *Elektrotechn. Z.* **11**, 412 (1959); *Kunststoffberater* **5**, 350 (1960); *Angew. Chem.* **74**, 647 (1962).
5. D. A. McLean, H. G. Wehe, and B. T. Dante, *IRE Trans. Component Pts.,* 89 (June 1961).
6. A. Ossenbrunner, H. Schnell, H. Klockgether, J. Geiger, and H. J. Freier (to Agfa A. G.), Ger. Pat. Appl. 1,001,586 (1957); A. Ossenbrunner, H. Klockgether, J. Geiger, H. Schnell, and H. J. Freier (to Agfa A. G.), Fr. Pat. 75,180 (1957).
7. A. Ossenbrunner, J. Geiger, and H. Klockgether (to Agfa A. G.), Fr. Pat. 1,205,938 (1958); A. Ossenbrunner, J. Geiger, and H. Klockgether (to Agfa A. G.), Ger. Pat. Appl. 1,064,806 (1959).
8. J. R. Waring and R. P. Easton (to General Aniline and Film Corp.), U. S. Pat. 3,005,787 (1961); A. M. Winchel (to General Aniline and Film Corp.), Belg. Pat. 604,361 (1961).
9. R. Blank, *Agfa, Repro-Mitt.* **9**, Heft 14, 1 (1961).
10. W. Hechelhammer and H. Streib (to Farbenfabriken Bayer A. G.), Belg. Pat. 603,329 (1961).
11. W. Abeck, A. Ossenbrunner, H. Klockgether, J. Geiger, and H. Schnell (to Agfa A. G.), U. S. Pat. 2,991,198 (1961); W. Abeck, A. Ossenbrunner, J. Geiger, H. Klockgether, and H. Schnell (to Agfa A. G.), Fr. Pat. 74,939 (1959).
12. G. Peilstöcker and W. Hechelhammer (to Farbenfabriken Bayer A. G.), U. S. Pat. 2,964,797 (1960); Anon., *Kunststoffberater* **4**, 420 (1959); W. Land, *Neue Verpackung* **14**, 330 (1961); W. Land, *Kunststoffberater* **6**, 135 (1961).
13. O. Jordan, *Kunststoffe* **47**, 521 (1957).
14. H. Klockgether, E. Bock, and W. Cohnen (to Agfa A. G.), Belg. Pat. 595,614 (1959).
15. J. J. Drittenbass, Brit. Pat. 864,682 (1961).
16. W. Hechelhammer and G. Peilstöcker (to Farbenfabriken Bayer A. G.), U. S. Pat. 2,991,273 (1961).
17. A. Thiel, *Plastverarbeiter* **7**, 54, 137, 269, 372, 418 (1956); A. Thiel, *Grundzüge der Vakuumverformung,* Verlag Brandenburger, Landau, 1957.
18. W. Neitzert, *Plastverarbeiter* **11**, 261 (1960); **12**, 5 (1961).
19. Firmenschrift "Makrolon" der Farbenfabriken Bayer A. G. (1960).
20. W. F. Christopher and D. W. Fox, *Polycarbonates,* Reinhold, New York, 1962.
21. W. Hechelhammer and G. Peilstöcker, *Kunststoffe* **49**, 3, 93 (1959).
22. W. Backofen, *Kunststoffe* **49**, 664 (1959).
23. W. Backofen, *Kunststoffe* **52**, 98 (1962).
24. E. F. Fiedler, W. F. Christopher, and T. R. Calkins, *Mod. Plastics* **36**, 115 (April 1959).
25. W. Backofen, *Ind. Plastiques, Mod. (Paris)* **12**, 61 (1960).
26. H. W. Streib, *British Plastics* **33**, 406 (1960).
27. W. Backofen, *Plastverarbeiter* **12**, 1, 55, 105 (1961).
28. W. Backofen, *Kunststoffe* **51**, 728 (1961).
29. W. Backofen, *Plastics* **26**, 71 (1961).
30. W. Woebecken, *Kunststoffe* **51**, 547 (1961).
31. W. Backofen and W. Schröder, *Kunststoffe* **52**, 29 (1962).
32. B. P. Jibben, (to N. V. Onderzoekingsinstituut Research), U. S. Pat. 3,021,303 (1962).

33. L. Bottenbruch, G. Fritz, and H. Schnell (to Farbenfabriken Bayer A. G.), Belg. Pat. 591,371 (1960).
34. Anon., *Mod. Plastics* **37,** 81 (April 1960).
35. H. W. Streib, *Chem. Ind.* **11,** 463 (1959).
36. B. Waeser, *Kunststoffe-Plastics* **6,** 57 (1959).
37. Anon., *Mod. Plastics* **37,** 172 (December 1959).
38. R. P. Sonderman, *Mod. Plastics* **36,** 136 (August 1959).
39. Anon., *Mod. Plastics* **37,** 102 (July 1960).
40. H. W. Streib, *Gummi, Asbest, Kunststoffe* **14,** 304 (1961).
41. Anon., *Mod. Plastics* **38,** 87 (April 1961); **39,** 84 (December 1961); **39,** 179 (September 1961).
42. A. D. Thomas and C. V. Leunig, *SPE J.* **18,** 1464 (1962).
43. H. Schnell, H. J. Rehberg, and W. Hechelhammer (to Farbenfabriken Bayer A. G.), Ger. Pat. 1,046,254 (1959).
44. H. Ritze, G. Franz, and W. Kühl, *Deutsche zahnärztl. Z.* **17,** 106 (1962).
45. W. Hechelhammer and H. Streib (to Farbenfabriken Bayer A. G.), Belg. Pat. 597,653 (1960).
46. G. Peilstöcker and W. Hechelhammer (to Farbenfabriken Bayer A. G.), U. S. Pat. 2,964,794 (1960).
47. S. Jarby and E. Andersen, *J. Dental Res.* **41,** 214 (1962).
48. G. Gruenwald, *Mod. Plastics* **38,** 137 (1960).
49. V. Böllert, G. Fritz, H. Schnell, and H. G. Lotter (to Farbenfabriken Bayer A. G.), Belg. Pat. 615,920 (1962); V. Böllert, G. Fritz, and H. Schnell, Ger. Pat. Appl., 1,133,727 (1962).
50. Belg. Pat. 559,115, Farbenfabriken Bayer A. G., (1957); A. Cooper, *Plastics Inst.* (*London*), *Trans. J.* **29,** 39 (1961).
51. H. Schnell, W. Geilenkirchen, C. Niehaus, and H. Krimm (to Farbenfabriken Bayer A. G.), Ger. Pat. 1,074,178 (1961).
52. N. C. Bolgiano (to Armstrong Cork Co.), U. S. Pats. 3,070,563 (1962), 3,071,556 (1963).
53. J. K. Sears and J. R. Darby, *Techn. Papers* **9,** II, 2 (1963).
54. H. Kramer, W. Eisenlohr, and H. Schnell (to Farbenfabriken Bayer A. G.), Ger. Pat. 1,076,329 (1960).
55. Brit. Pat. 834,502, Agfa A. G. (1960).
56. H. Schnell and H. J. Freier (to Farbenfabriken Bayer A. G.), Ger. Pat. 1,041,245 (1960).
57. H. Schnell, G. Fritz, and G. Peilstöcker (to Farbenfabriken Bayer A. G.), Ger. Pat. 1,100,949 (1961).

AUTHOR INDEX

209

SUBJECT INDEX

Acetaldehyde, condensation with phenol, 79

Acetone, condensation with phenol, 78, 80, 84

Acetylene, condensation with aromatic hydroxy compounds, 85

Acoyl cyanides, condensation with aromatic hydroxy compounds, 80

Acroleine, condensation with phenol, 79

Activation energy for viscous flow of molten bisphenol A polycarbonate, 125

Adipic acid, polyesters from, 3

Aging of bisphenol A polycarbonate, 63, 180–183

Air, influence on aromatic polycarbonates, 63, 180, 181, 182

Aluminum chloride, condensing agent for bisphenol preparation, 78

Annealing of bisphenol A polycarbonate, 129

influence on mechanical properties, 144, 180–183

Applications, for injection molded parts of bisphenol A polycarbonate, 197

for bisphenol A polycarbonate film, 190

Arc resistance of injection molded bisphenol A polycarbonate parts, 158

Base plane of the unit cell of bisphenol A polycarbonate, 135

Bc-plane of the unit cell of bisphenol A polycarbonate, 136

Benzaldehyde, condensation with phenol, 79

Benzoyl cyanide, condensation with aromatic hydroxy compounds, 80

Biological activity of bisphenol A polycarbonate, 184

Bis-alkyl carbonates of aliphatic dihydroxy compounds, 16, 18

Bis-aryl carbonates, of aliphatic-aromatic dihydroxy compounds, 24, 25

of aliphatic dihydroxy compounds, 16, 18

of aromatic dihydroxy compounds, 51

Bis-chlorocarbonic acid esters, adducts with pyridine, 12

adducts with tertiary amines, 12, 13

as intermediates for aliphatic polycarbonates, 10, 13

as intermediates for aromatic polycarbonates, 38, 41

as intermediates for block copolycarbonates, 54

as intermediates for polycarbonate copolymers, 56

reaction with water, 11

Bis-(4-hydroxy-3-carboxylic acid phenyl ester)-phenyl methane in crosslinkable polycarbonate copolymers, 64, 65

Bisphenol A, see 4,4'-Dihydroxy diphenyl-2,2-propane

Bis-trichloromethyl carbonate, 14, 41, 92

Block copolycarbonates, 54

of various aromatic dihydroxy compounds, 55, 68

Blow molding of bisphenol A polycarbonate, 201

Bonding of Bisphenol A polycarbonate film, 193

Boron fluoride, condensing agent for bisphenol preparation, 78, 80, 84

Brittleness temperature of bisphenol A polycarbonate, 145

n,iso-Butyraldehyde, condensation with phenol, 79

Capacitors, bisphenol A polycarbonate as dielectric for, 192

Carbontetrachloride, reaction with phenol, 92